MONSTER POETRY

Scotland

Edited by Donna Samworth

First published in Great Britain in 2014 by:

 Young**Writers**

Remus House
Coltsfoot Drive
Peterborough
PE2 9BF
Telephone: 01733 890066
Website: www.youngwriters.co.uk

Printed and bound in the UK by BookPrintingUK
Website: www.bookprintinguk.com

Foreword

Young Writers was established in 1991, dedicated to encouraging reading and creative writing by young people. Our nationwide writing initiatives are designed to inspire ideas and the incentive to write, and in turn develop literacy skills and confidence, whilst participating in a fun, imaginative activity. The final reward is the opportunity for the budding young writer to see their work in print.

Our latest competition, *Monster Poetry,* focuses on uncovering the different techniques used in poetry and encouraging pupils to explore new ways to write a poem. Using a mix of imagination, expression and poetic styles, this anthology is an impressive snapshot of the inventive, original and skilful writing of young people today. We hope this collection will delight readers for years to come.

Contents

**Aberlady Primary
School, Longniddry**

Alek Jardine 1
Amy Mitchell 2
Beth Douglas (12) 2
Arron Darge (10) 3
Ben Kauffmann (10) 3
Charlotte Rogers 4
Elizabeth Austin 4
Emma Niven 5
Georgia Rafferty 5
Eve Smart (11) 6
Flossie Coltart 7
Hannah Innes (10) 8
Imogen Mason 9
Kate Latto 10
Lucy Scott (12) 11
Luke Verrall 11
Olivia Sinclair 12

**Bowhouse Primary
School, Grangemouth**

Travis Wylie (11) 13
Eilidh Gallacher (11) 14
Kaitlin Anderson (11) 15
Ciera McDonald (11) 15
Drew Cummings (11) 16
Kyle Thomson (11) 16
Claudia Davidson (11) 17
Robert Wrigley (11) 18

**Carbost Primary School,
Isle Of Skye**

Sarajayne Edmondson (10) 19

Collace Primary School, Perth

Katie McVean (10) 20
Lilian Mailer (9) 20
Amy McVean (8) 21
Christopher Hally (6) 21
Ryan Cree (11) 22
Sophie Hutchison (10) 22
Jessica Brown (10) 23

Reuben Whiteside (9) 24
Charlie Timoney (7) 24
Evie Mullen (9) 25
Finn Anderson (6) 25
Nathan Preston (9) 26
Katie Cree (9) 27

**Culbokie Primary
School, Dingwall**

Fergus Whiteside (10) 28
Paige Kennedy (8) 28
Kaitlin Grant (10) 29
James Barling (9) 29
Jenny Czerniakiewicz (10) 30

Forehill Primary School, Ayr

Karli Prendergast (7) 31
Chloe McGinnis (7) 31
Ava Paterson (7) 31
Aodán McGeechan (7) 32
Jack McKinnon (9) 32
Douglas McKinnon (9) 33
Cole Love (9) 33
Holly Mackie (7) 34
Lauren Eva Sives (7) 34
Rachael Duffin (7) 34
Dylan Roberts (7) 35
Chloe Greenwood (7) 35
Cameron Sym (8) 35
Max Mason (7) 36
Lyell King (7) 36
Ryan McGeachin (9) 37
Zack Graham (9) 37
Callum Boyd (9) 38
Abbie Boyd (9) 38
Sarah Connell (9) 39
Jenna Currie (9) 39
Curtis Neave (9) 40
Adam Meek (9) 40
Alexander Burns (9) 41
Samuel Drummond (9) 41
Brendan Kong (9) 42
Claudia Coulter (9) 42

Liam Mackie (9) 43
Niamh McIntosh (9) 43
Kaitlyn Brown (10) 44
Brooke Smillie (9) 44
Brooke Cunningham (9) 45
Carla Russell (9) 45
Tyler Aryee (9) 46
Rhys Johnston (9) 46
Lora McNamee (9) 47
Shannon McLaughlin (9) 47
Ryan Keating (9) 48

**Furnace Primary
School, Inveraray**
Ninamarie Crossey (9) 48
Samantha Knight (9) 49

**Glencairn Primary
School, Stevenston**
Mollie Ford (10) 49
Sophie Doherty (10) 50
Rachel Irvine (11) 50
Jhena Dickie (10) 51
Luke Wakenell (10) 51
Abby Wallace (11) 52
Keirin Bramwell (11) 52
Paige Simson (11) 53
Ryan Watt (8) 53
Ashley Smith (10) 54
Jamie Johnson (8) 54
Gemma Irvine (8) 55
Logan Stoney (8) 55
Katie Mortimer (8) 56
Matthew Boyd (11) 56
Raymond McLaughlin (8) 57
Rebecca Baird (10) 57
Hollie McGinn 58

**Greenview Special
School, Glasgow**
James McNeil 59

**Halfmerke Primary
School, East Kilbride**
Aidan Shaw (10) 60
Connor Pollock (10) 60
Katie Smith (10) 61
Brian Robertson (10) 62

Ciara Young (10) 63
Iona McDougall (10) 64
Cairnie Glaister (10) 64
Jackson Leishman (10) 65
Lewis Borthwick (10) 65
Rachel Green (10) 66
Jennifer Marshall (10) 67
Orla McHugh (10) 68
Emma Scott (10) 69
Ciaran McClure (10) 70
Robbie Bell (10) 71
Katie Young (10) 72
Jamie Jeffrey (10) 72
Dean McIlraith (9) 73
Andrew Shuff (10) 73

Insch School, Insch
Sandy Griffin (10) 74
Archie Wilson (10) 75
Dylan Craig (9) 75
Ben Forsyth (10) 76
Charlotte Comber (10) 77
Freya Ogilvie (9) 78
Harry Macduff (9) 78
Eve Fraser (10) 79
David McLeod (9) 79
Emily McGlashan (8) 80
Hugo Ricketts (10) 81
Aimee Duguid (10) 82
Josh Cannell (10) 83
Molly Underwood (9) 84
Tom Kolsch (9) 84
Luke Godwin (9) 85

**Milton Of Leys Primary
School, Inverness**
Lois Taylor (8) 85
Jack Hamilton (9) 86
Kirsten McKay (9) 86
Gemma Birnie (9) 87
Logan Ross (9) 87
Nilavan Tamijmarane (8) 88
Liam Moodie (9) 88
Amy Skeoch (9) 89
Darren Calder (9) 89
Tyler Clare (8) 90
Luke Seago (9) 90
Maddison Cameron (9) 91

Joe Dickinson (9) 91
Rachel Bailey (9) 92
William Urquhart (9) 93
Sharleen Kennedy (9) 94
Naomi Stewart (9) 95
Beth Mackenzie (10) 96
Leah Hollister (9) 97
Freya MacLennan (10) 98
Emily Willox (9) 98
Robbie Fraser (9) 99
Kieran Watson (9) 99
Jonathan Williams (10) 100
Gabrielle MacDonald (9) 100
Amy Coats (9) 101
Megan Baxter (9) 101
Leah Collingwood (9) 102
Katie Grant (9) 103
Brooke Fraser (8) 104
Ewan Brown (9) 105
Owen MacDonald (8) 106
Lennon Mackay (8) 106
Ellie Ross (9) 107
Ben Stainsby (9) 107
Duncan (9) 108
Macy Mercer (9) 109
Katie Ward 110
Rhianna Parker (10) 111
Susan Gardocka (9) 112
Max Tasasiz (8) 113
Charlie Lawson (9) 114
Orla Buchanan (9) 114
Mia Cunningham (9) 115

Monkton Primary School, Prestwick

Grace Wellwood Guy (8) 115
Emma Coulter (8) 116
Lauren Cooper (7) 116
Emily Wilson (8) 117
Amy Holland (8) 117
Reece Merry (8) 118
Beth Kerr (8) 118
Nathan Lydon (8) 119
Laura Baker (7) 119
Caitlin Taylor (9) 120
Stephen McDonnell (7) 120
Lia Latimer (8) 121

Jacob Mullen (7) 121
Katie Baker (8) 122
Sandy Crann (8) 122
Joseph Murray (7) 123
Ben Thomson (8) 123
Grace Kerr (8) 124

Onthank Primary School, Kilmarnock

Hannah Robinson (9) 124
Amy MacDonald (10) 125
Charlie Muirhead (9) 125
Kyle Stewart McCrone (9) 126
Alicia Cree (9) 126
Jenna Allan (9) 127
Caitlyn Oueay (9) 127
Emily Campbell (9) 128
Tjay Hastings (9) 129
Austin Reid (9) 130
Alexander Leslie (9) 130
Glenn McPheator (9) 131
Eva McQuade (9) 131
Liam Davies (10) 132
Louise Milligan (9) 132
Meg Sinclair (9) 133
Kyle Bryden (10) 133
Tamzyn Thomson (9) 134

Riverside Primary School, Stirling

Brogan Henderson (9) 134
Liam Fraser (9) 135
Erin Bechelli (9) 135
Callum Addison (9) 136
Georgina Robertson (9) 136

St Brendan's Primary RC School, Glasgow

Kayleigh Trainer (8) 137
Sinead Monaghan (9) 137
Leah McGill (8) 138
Kieran Hinton (8) 138
Connor Hudson (8) 139
Adam Gillon (8) 139
Jacob Seabright (8) 140
Agata Knaak (8) 140
Connor Cassidy (7) 141
John Smith (8) 141
Aidan Milne (8) 142

Caleb Lyden (8) 142
Ruby Gallagher (7) 143
Kenzo Warren (7) 143
Kyle Irumwa (8) 144

Shawhead Primary School, Dumfries

Callum Ross (5)..................................... 144
India Woods (5) 145
Samuel Johnstone-Wilcox (7)............... 145
Emily Jahn (7).. 146
Harry Greenwood (7)............................ 147

Strathpeffer Primary School, Strathpeffer

Noah Henry (11) 148
Emily Forrest (10).................................. 149
Jody MacLean (10)................................ 150
Elsa Fearn (10)...................................... 151
Nicole Nicol (10) 151
Lara Lamont (10) 152
Tigerlily Potter (10) 152

Strone Primary School, Dunoon

Charlie Carlin (9) 153
Owen Danks (10)................................... 153
Kimberley Frederick (10) 153
Duncan Morgan (11)............................. 154
Abigail Stone (11) 154
Ciaran Danks (11).................................. 155
Campbell Morgan (9)............................ 155
Cameron Harding (9)............................ 156

Stuartfield School, Peterhead

Cerys Hayes (11)................................... 156
Isaac McLean (11) 157
Brooke Erridge (11) 157
Scott Robertson (11)............................. 158
Jamie Kindness (11) 158
Nicholas Elrick (10)............................... 158
Georgia Hay (11) 159
Caillen McLean (12) 159
Kelly Rebecca (10) 160
Sophie McCallum (12).......................... 160
Jack Bain (12).. 161

Tollbrae Primary School, Airdrie

Aasiyah Rehman (11)............................ 161
Anthony Fitzgerald (12) 162
Cameron MacPherson (11) 162
Daniel Stanners (11).............................. 163
Donald Obre (11) 163
Erin O'Neill (11)..................................... 164
Jamie Ford (11) 164
Rebecca Milton (12) 165

The Poems

Monster In Black

There's a big monster who works for MIB
If you're not nice he will eat you for tea!
But if you are good, he is lots of fun
He is really quite young, only 21!
Quite scary and tall, he's six foot ten
Has the strength of three ordinary men
One of his missions was to fly to Mars,
Off into space, oh so far
He came back to Earth,
And arrived on home turf.
He went to HQ to get his medal,
But unfortunately a villain started to meddle
His boss sent him to kill,
And make him pay the evil bill.
The villain laughed at him you see,
So the monster ate him for tea.
He grew old and decided to retire,
So he told his boss, McIntyre.
He was asked to do one more job
Which involved him travelling the globe.
He had to find a monster who could be,
The next best agent in MIB!

Alek Jardine
Aberlady Primary School, Longniddry

The Best Monster

I know a monster called Isla . . .

She is the very best
She is much better than all the rest
We always walk to school together
We will do that forever.

Isla has cute fuzzy hair
And a personality which means she will always care
She may not be the biggest monster
But for me, she's always there

Another thing about this creature
There are lots of things that I can teach her
One day I looked under my bed
And with a great big sigh she said . . .

'I love you Amy!'

Amy Mitchell
Aberlady Primary School, Longniddry

My Friendly Marshmallow

His glimmering eyes peering at the pink and white pack
Darting, fleetingly, never looking back
His stripy, green bobble hat
He looked as if he wanted to chat.

I walked into the store
It was quite a bore
Waiting in line
But I get home, just in time.

We went to the park
And ate the pink and white pack,
He smiled at me and I smiled back.

Beth Douglas (12)
Aberlady Primary School, Longniddry

The Slim Slime

There once was a very sad slime
Who was born on Planet Mars
But he looked so ugly because
He munched too many chocolate bars,

Then one day, fed up of living on Mars
He moved to the Earth and the Moon
He stuffed his face with Mars bars
And grew chubby, all too soon

Then people started calling him names
It made him really sad
He wanted to be friends with the people
He wanted it really quite bad

But soon from Finland to France
They all became his friends
Everyone started to dance
So the slim slime got thin in the end.

Arron Darge (10)
Aberlady Primary School, Longniddry

The Thing

Down from the mountain of Zog
Out through the winter fog
There came The Thing with its little feet
Walking down the moonlit street
It looked lonely in every way
Now it has chosen to come and stay
The Thing walks down the street
Wondering who he will meet
He much prefers the night
And when the sun begins to rise
He settles down and closes his eyes

So if ever you're out for a walk
And meet The Thing . . . do stop and talk!

Ben Kauffmann (10)
Aberlady Primary School, Longniddry

Him And Me

My best friend Feo is from the planet of Splash
He came to Earth with a mighty big crash!
In my garden is where he lay
Feo stood up wanting to play

His spotted wellies were very mucky
He chose my garden, I felt very lucky
He pulled my hand with a fluffy grip
Took me to a puddle and made me tip

I fell in with a splash
I jumped up, it made him laugh!
Giggling away he jumped in
He slipped over into the bin

The next day we went to the park
Paddling away in the dark
I invited him home for some tea
That was the start of him and me!

Charlotte Rogers
Aberlady Primary School, Longniddry

My Monster

My monster and me
Sat on a tree
We ate some food
This put us in a good mood

I saw his house out at sea
Where he invited me
To his home, cosy and hot
Where we played games quite a lot

Henry is my monster's name
His favourite TV show is Fame
We have fun when we play
I love you Henry, hip hooray!

Elizabeth Austin
Aberlady Primary School, Longniddry

Monster In A Box

When I got home Mum was baking some cakes
Dad had a box, he asked me to take
Excited and happy, I opened it up
A hamster? A kitten? As cute little pup?

Inside was a monster
We were happy to meet
My dad smiled and told me
'I found him on the street.'

I gave him my headphones
And went up to bed
He slept on my pillow
He liked to rest his head

Everyone loves my monster
He's really quite cool
Furry and cute, he's quite small
Friendly and funny, not very tall.

Emma Niven
Aberlady Primary School, Longniddry

Bobble The Clever Monster

My monster and me
Swam under the sea
I saw his home
Where he lives alone

He took off his hat
And sat on a fluffy mat
I asked him, 'Help me with my homework please.'
As I sat down next to him, on my knees

'Of course!' he said with a smile
'Even though this may take a while.'
Thank you Bobble! At last it's the end
I love you Bobble, my little fuzzy friend!

Georgia Rafferty
Aberlady Primary School, Longniddry

Me And Splodge

They landed in my garden
The monsters, you see
But it wasn't just her alone,
Not one . . . three!
But they left Splodge all alone
Her happy voice turning into a sad and lonely tone
So I kept her as my very own pet
I learned very quickly you can't take her to the vet
We've been to lots of places
Just her and me
Like London for example
The London Eye, what can you see!
We also went to Paris
Just her and me
And shared a big baguette
Washed down with a cup of tea
We also went to Sydney
Just her and me
And we had a big picnic
Under an apple tree
The stench of burgers and hot dogs
At the summer BBQ
And that again
Was just her and me
She scared a lot of people
I know she doesn't mean to though
She may look very scary
But she's the kindest monster I know.

Eve Smart (11)
Aberlady Primary School, Longniddry

Mizzy The Monster

Mizzy is a type of monster
Found in flowers and trees
In the summer Mizzy appears
Leaves with the winter freeze

One day in the summer a Mizzy was found
And taken far away
Her magic was drained and stolen
And she was put in a cage to play

In this cage there were other monsters
Brown and blue and beige
Scary ones and angry ones
They didn't want to play

Little did the humans know
That Mizzy had more magic
Just enough to break the bars
Such a clever tactic!

Sneak past the humans
And get the magic back
Make a little potion
Hear it fizzle, pop and crack!

The little Mizzy ran away
And found her way back home
She went to find her mum and dad
Never more to roam.

Flossie Coltart
Aberlady Primary School, Longniddry

The Little Monster

Last night a monster came to town
Said his spaceship had fallen down
It was a very happy day
When my monster came to stay

But winter weather is cold and grey
Too frosty and chilly to go out to play
Suddenly, my monster wandered off
Freezing cold as he began to cough

I gave him a hug to keep him warm
And to feel safe from the rain storm
I tucked us up inside a cave
We both felt we were very brave

Now time has passed and we're still friends
Together, forever, right up to the end
I won't let my monster out of my sight
'I love you!' I tell him, and hug him tight.

Hannah Innes (10)
Aberlady Primary School, Longniddry

Monster University

My monster is called Sophie
She comes from Happy Land
She loves to walk beside me
She likes to hold my hand

Sophie has a friend called Sue
They go to university together
They travel there, come rain or shine
In all kinds of weather

They love to go to science lessons
They like to go to maths
They like to learn a lot of things
They listen well in class

When I grow up I'd like to learn
To study with Sophie and Sue
So now I'll stick in hard at school
And do my homework too.

Imogen Mason
Aberlady Primary School, Longniddry

Zing

I walked into my room
Suddenly there was a boom
I went over to my bed
And saw a fluffy head

He said, 'My name is Zing!
What are you? A strange looking thing!'
I said, 'My name is Sam,
You can come out if you are calm.'

I said, 'You can come to school
But you must obey the rules.'
And so he came with me
And my classmates laughed with glee.

My friends said, 'Wow! He's really cool!'
They loved Zing at my school
And at the end of the day
We all went home to play

And then the news was bad
I felt so very sad
Zing had to go away
'Goodbye!' was all he'd say

I cried and called for Zing
But I've never heard anything
My poem is at an end
It's sad to lose a friend.

Kate Latto
Aberlady Primary School, Longniddry

He Used To Be Mine

Lurking around at the bottom of my bed,
A little pink monster sticks out its small head,
My monster is lovely and kind you see,
Not fierce and dangerous or hurtful to me,

But I lost my monster when I was out and about,
I cried and I yelled and I even did shout,
I ran home and found him under my bed,
'Where have you been?' I worriedly said,

'I met up with your brother, he's ever so kind!'
'What about me?' I pleaded and whined,
'You're too old for me now! Your brother needs me,'
Now my brother has a monster, he's only three!

Lucy Scott (12)
Aberlady Primary School, Longniddry

Eating The Children

Everyone had just walked into class,
And started doing maths,
Then our teacher walked out,
And some of the other children seemed to be in doubt,
She was soon replaced with a small furry monster who seemed rather nice,
But he didn't seem much of a teacher because he smelt of rice
One by one he took the children out,
But they didn't return as if they'd been eaten inside out.
Some of the children think the teacher is making a big fault,
Those children were nice, although they needed some salt.

Luke Verrall
Aberlady Primary School, Longniddry

My Little Monster

I found my little monster
In my garden pond
And while we've been together
We've grown a special bond!

You see, my little monster
Is slippery and green
He is very grumpy
Like none you've ever seen!

In a tank my monster lives
And sleeps in a little deck chair
Swims like a squid, my monster does
With his tufts of ginger hair!

But now my monster has a wife
We don't see each other anymore
He has to look after his children
Playing alone is such a bore!

I still love my monster
And I know he loves me too
But little monsters must grow up
Just like me and you!

Olivia Sinclair
Aberlady Primary School, Longniddry

Asteroid X

Asteroid X has crashed
It shook, rattled and flashed
Rocks flying everywhere
All around the air
But suddenly there was a creature
As adorable as a puppy

It was standing there
As frozen as ice
It was all hairy
So I suspected lots of lice
It was red and had orange, small pointy ears
It was exactly the image of my sister's fears

Suddenly he landed on top of my head
I was really scared, I thought I was dead
But then something magical happened
Something I didn't expect
I started to levitate
Yes, I'm correct!

I wanted to keep him as a pet
I wanted to call him Guntar
And that's the story of how
Me and Guntar lived
Happily ever after.

Travis Wylie (11)
Bowhouse Primary School, Grangemouth

Rainbow Robyn And All Her Friends

Ah! Look at you, you are fluffy all round
You go red, orange, yellow, purple and blue right to the ground
You're so adorable, I want to take you home
But you need to go back where other monsters roam

You fly so high I cannae see
Don't fall down, you will bang into a tree
Your colourful body is so cute
I like you, I'm in a suit

Rainbow Robyn has so many friends
Her happiness never ends
Her very best friend is Rainbow Dash
She has a best friend Sash
Rainbow Robyn has a pet owl
Her name is Ollie and she is a-growl

She goes to Earth to help out
The children she helps give a scream and a shout
The children never have any fear
And the babies ha! Never have a tear
Her heart is so strong
She meditates with a gong

There you go, she saved the day
None of the children need to pay
'Hooray, hooray, she saved the day.'

Eilidh Gallacher (11)
Bowhouse Primary School, Grangemouth

Huggle Has A Plan!

The Earthlings are waiting
For a fearsome beast to attack
In the rock bushes of Jupiter
I heard someone or something rustling about on Mars

Who could that be?
I wondered to myself
So I thought I would go over
And see who the someone or something was

When I was on Mars
I was looking about
Crash!
I turned around with such fear
And there it stood

It was a blue, horrifying beast
It looked as slimy as a snake
His gigantic blue eyes stared at me
I knew it was going to attack.

Kaitlin Anderson (11)
Bowhouse Primary School, Grangemouth

The Shadow Creeper

You better watch out when near a shadow
Believe me they're mad though
They may look harmless but you will be terrified
When you find out the truth of the shadow creeper
I hope that you'll never be there with the creeper
He's as tall as a tower and as loud as a keeper
They're not good sleepers
At night they will come to your house and up your slippery stairs
You won't hear them no one does
They're as quick as a mouse, but as careful as a doctor
No one will hear you shout, all they will hear is the sound of you going out
It will be a lesson very well learned
Not to go near a shadow when out.

Ciera McDonald (11)
Bowhouse Primary School, Grangemouth

Monster Poem

As red as blood
If you touch he will turn green or blue
And he is about five foot two
He likes Portugal but he likes the sound of spectacular Scotland too
He likes to lie in bed
And he likes the colour red

He likes the beach
But he doesn't like a peach
If he touches sand or water
He will die

Then he wants to go to Belmont with P7
And he goes
And he grows and grows
And he meets a friend called Gunter
Gunter is a friendly monster just like me.

Drew Cummings (11)
Bowhouse Primary School, Grangemouth

Superhero Sully

I am a superhero
I glow in the dark
I have lots of friends
But they're all in the park
Batman plays on the swing
While I play with my ring
All the other monsters are having a drink!

I am blue with pink spots
Batman is black with yellow spots
He likes to save animals
I like to save people
We are as careful as a dentist!

Kyle Thomson (11)
Bowhouse Primary School, Grangemouth

Fuz

Deep in the Merry Meadows
Fuz the kind creature follows
Butterflies come and tickle him with laughter
He'll have a snooze after
Butterflies leave with a ting with their wing
All in the good season of spring
Snoozing away with a bunny on his belly
The swaying of the trees wake him up early
Staring at the bunny with kindness
He gave off the scent of sweet violets
As he watched the bunny toddle away
With the trees there he swayed.

Summertime was here at last
Fuz had such a blast!
He went to the beach when the stars were out
So humans didn't scream and shout
He wiggled his toes in the sand
He cupped the water with his hand
The water crept and kissed his feet
While he had a burger to eat.

Cold months are coming round
A new house must be found
A log house with a chimney
And a fireplace lovely
Snuggle up with a blanket
Fuz had hot chocolate and he drank it
Now it's time for a snooze
Until springtime I hope it's soon.

Claudia Davidson (11)
Bowhouse Primary School, Grangemouth

Green Green Goofy

Goofy has no friends
He says the sadness never ends
Until he saw me
He came running to me

Goofy said, 'Hello! I taste like jello,'
Then we became friends – the fun never ends!
Goofy said, 'Thank you for being my friend'
I said, 'No bother, the laughs will suffice!'

We went to town
Goofy wore brown
'Green, green Goofy,' sung Goofy
I joined in, we sang like angels

We started to get hungry, I started to moan
Goofy said, 'Calm down take a bite of my toe.'
I started to smell a stench in the air
I said, 'What on Earth is that?'

He said, 'I'm really sorry I haven't eaten my greens
When I don't eat them I smell like mouldy cheese.'
So I sprayed him with DO
He no longer smelled like BO

So after a great day
He had to hit the hay
'I'll see you tomorrow,' I said
He said, 'It's not that easy . . . '

Robert Wrigley (11)
Bowhouse Primary School, Grangemouth

Monster Fun

Todd the monster is as blue as the sky
He is fuzzy, friendly, funny and smelly
He is even bigger than the trees
And he does not like bees
His belly jiggles like a jelly,

Todd has some monster friends
They are friendly but not as friendly as him
He has a friend called Molly
They have done lots of things together,

Todd and Molly hear noises
They hide behind a bush
Molly falls!
Oh dear, but she's alright,

Todd has many monster friends
As many as you can imagine
Even if they are really big
It is how they are inside,

One of Todd's friends got hurt
He got a scratch and some bruises
Molly was so scared
She ran away
Then when Todd's friend was better
She came back,

Molly made friends with Todd's friend
They went to the park and had fun
Then they go to Molly's house
And have lots of parties.

Sarajayne Edmondson (10)
Carbost Primary School, Isle Of Skye

Sly's Wish

There once was a cat named Sly
Who wished he could fly very high
He was cunning and smart
And often liked a tart
There once was a cat named Sly

He wished his wish and soon it came true
He flew up high and saw the sea blue
He was like a big bird way up in the sky
And he shouted out loud, 'Oh my, oh my!'

He flew a long way, out to the jungle
And soon he was lost and in a big jumble
He heard a big roar from a massive striped tiger
And flew in the clouds up high, even higher!

His wings stopped working and he got very tired
And realised that his energy had expired
He was left in the jungle all alone by himself
And wanted that magic lamp he had left on his shelf

That was the end of Sly's luxury life
And his great big house way down in East Fife
So just remember all explorers out there
There still might be another Sly – so do take care!

Katie McVean (10)
Collace Primary School, Perth

Moody Monster

One day a monster was in a bad mood
He was so grumpy
He would not eat his food
But Lilian was good at cheering monsters up
So she made a funny face
The monster thought she looked great
Lilian felt ace!

Lilian Mailer (9)
Collace Primary School, Perth

Cutie My Monster

On the way to the store I met a purple monster
She took me and my friends to toy land

We ate sweets and got free toys and climbed a tree
We saw talking flowers

We went for a swim in the huge big teddy pool
It was really cool

We saw a baby deer that had lost its dummy
But we later found its mummy

Then we had tea and went home with Cutie
My purple sharp-clawed monster.

Amy McVean (8)
Collace Primary School, Perth

A Day Out With My Monster

The day I spent with my monster
Was a very special day
We went to the park
We saw cars on the way
Then we climbed up the tallest climbing frame
We saw cars and trees from the top
We heard buses and lorries
We felt metal, it made us stop
We smelt oil
We tasted smoke
Then I hoped
It was all a joke.

Christopher Hally (6)
Collace Primary School, Perth

The Evil Master Sludge

It all started in a high tech city
Where underground, Sludge was plotting
As evil as a Tasmanian devil
Sludge laughed when his army was complete
Like a bull in a china shop the army pulled at hover cars
And pushed buildings
'It's only the beginning,' said Master Sludge
Laughing dastardly on his hover craft
But then out of the blue
A weird superhero attacked Master Sludge!
'*Noooo!*' cried Master Sludge
As the police arrested him
The city was restored to peace.

Ryan Cree (11)
Collace Primary School, Perth

What Do Monsters Do?

One day a monster went to the shops
He bought choco foam and lamb chops
In the supermarket everybody screamed
When his scary golden face beamed

When he got home
He put on the foam
He really enjoyed it
And then felt silly a bit

After dinner we had an ice cream
It was choco loco beam
It was time for bed
'Night, night,' he said.

Sophie Hutchison (10)
Collace Primary School, Perth

Cuddles The Orange Monster

Cuddles gasped at the TV screen
As the siren went *scream, scream*
A police car shot by the camera
To scare the riot-running llama
Cuddles tried to arrest his ted
Until we had to go to bed
His furry body was gone the next day
So I headed away
I ran to the police station
Passing Kirsty from 'Location Location'
I ended up in a huge commotion
And tripped on a bottle of hand lotion
From this level I could see Cuddles' feet
He was gnawing on a beet
I saw a robber wearing black
Outside the smashed windows of the bank
An orange shape hurtled towards him
A police sheriff cried, 'Whoa there, Jim.'
The robber grabbed him and shot round the bend
I tried to follow but was grabbed by a friend
She cried, 'Don't follow, he's got a gun!'
This was getting fun
Of course not
I ran away, grabbing a pot
He has a gun, I don't care
I wouldn't if he shut me in this lair
I got a glimpse of orange fur
Very far away, just a blur
I finally caught up and tackled the robber
Grabbing Cuddles and crying, 'G'day cobbler!'
I jumped, kicking his chin
Luckily not breaking the skin
The sheriff leaped over the fence
His strength, it was immense
He arrested the robber and gave me a grin
And tickled Cuddles under the chin
He said, 'Well done little 'un!'

Jessica Brown (10)
Collace Primary School, Perth

The Beetle Of The Year Award

Me and my dog were in the city
The beetle was in the desert
But the beetle found out
And he had no doubt
That he would win that golden shiny medal
But then I found out
And we had no doubt
That we could beat that big beetle
So the beetle came to town
And he heard a great big sound
Of us coming
But when we were coming we were humming
Which gave the monster the creeps
But we heard a sound
And Luna barked and howled
The beetle was too scared
And he went back
And that's the end of that.

Reuben Whiteside (9)
Collace Primary School, Perth

Evil American Monstahahaha!

The Evil American took short cuts
He had lunch which was pork chops
After lunch he destroyed planet Stilt
Then he robbed the kilt man of his kilt
He wore it all the next day
When he went out to play.

Charlie Timoney (7)
Collace Primary School, Perth

Rolo Saves The Planet Polo

Rolo Polo is a very spiky, cute animal,
She is very small, she could never be tall.
Her phone rang, it sang a song,
Rolo answered and said, 'Hello?'
He replied, 'It's your special agent Tom.'
Tom shouted, 'The walking owls of death are here,
Everybody is in total fear!'
'I will save them!
Uhh one question, where are they?'
'They are just passing the River Tay.'
'I'm on it,' said Rolo, 'I promise I won't go solo,'
Rolo saw them
She curled into a ball
They never saw her, she wasn't that tall
So the owls tripped over her
Believe me her skin did not feel like fur
Her pricks went right into their leg
So before anyone saw she fled
She got home as snug as a bug under her cosy little rug.

Evie Mullen (9)
Collace Primary School, Perth

My Monster Poem

I went out with my monster one day
To the park and on the slide
Where we had fun and played
On the way to McDonald's my monster tripped onto the road
But I was ever so bold
And saved him, the cute monster.

Finn Anderson (6)
Collace Primary School, Perth

Dreadful Disdon

One day in the underworld,
A monster called Disdon
Wanted an adventure.
He wanted to come
To the overworld.
The first place he came to was too hot,
He didn't like the tanning studio.
The second place he came to was too cold,
He didn't like the ice rink.
The third place he came to was too damp,
No, he didn't like the car wash.
The fourth place he came to was just too smelly,
He didn't like the dump.
He thinks maybe the underworld isn't that bad,
It's better than any of these places.
So, with a swish of a tentacle he left the overworld
To go back to the underworld.

Nathan Preston (9)
Collace Primary School, Perth

My Monster Tracy

I went to the beach with my monster one day
We went for a swim and had fun
We swam and splashed almost all day
But time went so fast, we didn't notice the sun
So we packed up and went to Burger King
When we got home I heard a noise but ignored it
Then I noticed it was a ring
I told Tracy to sit
She obeyed me and sat
I answered my phone
While Tracy chased the cat
It was Evie my BFF asking if I wanted to come over for a sleepover
I said yes and that night we did each other's hair and painted our nails
On my nails Evie painted a four leaf clover
The night went quickly and before I knew it, it was morning
We had breakfast and I went back home
And Tracy went into her dome home.

Katie Cree (9)
Collace Primary School, Perth

Flying Monsters

I walked out onto the dusty red planet
It turned dark within an hour,
I saw a flower by a tower,
Then I was taken by a great beast,
He flew me away to cook me,
I shouted, 'Hey,' but nothing happened
I tried kicking the monster and he dropped me into a cage with lots of other people,
I found out it was a feeding ground, people were getting eaten by the minute,
I saw a gap in the wooden bars,
I went towards the hole in the bars but it was a trap
More monsters flew down, I screamed,
A monster bit me and poisoned me,
Even though I was dying I made a run for it,
I could hear the monsters shrieking and they started to follow me
I got back to my ship and started the engine
I needed another fuel cell but the only fuel cell was in the feeding ground
I couldn't go back there, I would die
Luckily for me, a rescue ship came to save me, deep in space I was cured . . .

Fergus Whiteside (10)
Culbokie Primary School, Dingwall

The Frackle

I am a greedy, selfish and mean monster
I have no friends
I live in a dumpster that will never end
It is quite good to live in the dumpster
The food is good
Not so good with the banana peels
That's the worst part of living in the dumpster
But one day I smelt something good
It smelt lovely
It smelt like a steak
I had to have a sneak peek out the dumpster
I heard something crackle and frackle.

Paige Kennedy (8)
Culbokie Primary School, Dingwall

My Trip Through London

I was walking through London with my mum
When I saw a monster sucking its thumb
It asked me for ways to go
Then it stubbed its massive toe
And then it grabbed my hand
And stole 500 grand
It walked me right along the Thames
The stones at the bottom looked like gems
We held our heads high to see Big Ben
I shook like mad when the clock struck ten
We walked along the London Bridge
So cold I felt like a fridge
Going round in the London Eye
Eating a scrummy steak pie
We walked elegantly past Buckingham Palace
And we bumped into a lady called Alice
Alice was a friend of my mum
Wandering away with a monster I know now I was dumb.

Kaitlin Grant (10)
Culbokie Primary School, Dingwall

The Monster Poem

My monster is six foot high
And he is green with a scary face
His eyes glow red
Which match his feet
When he gets angry he blows right up then comes back
One day me and my monster had an idea
A wonderful idea
It was to take over the world
We made an invention but then there was a smell, a horrible smell
It smelt like rotten food
I turned around and it was my monster letting rip
I laughed at him then he got angry and blew right up and never came back
And that was the end of my monster.

James Barling (9)
Culbokie Primary School, Dingwall

The Scottish Monster

I am a Scottish monster,
One of the very best,
My name is Sammy McRednose,
But all my friends call me Slimy,
Just because I'm green,
I find that very mean.

One day we went to the park,
We were having such a lark,
Till we had a competition,
To see who could make the decision,
To go to the king's palace,
And steal the magnificent crown,
Which just now was covered in brown,
Brown, brown mud,
But it had a diamond stud,
Slap bang in the middle!
But it was a riddle,
How to get in . . .
Two minutes later we hid in the bin,
We've figured a way,
It took us the day,
But here we are now!
And then came the row . . .
'Well hello there Slimy!' the bully shouted out
'That bin quite suits you!' she teased,
'It might help you get a bit more grimy!'
'Get ready for the last day of your life!' he yelled with strife,
'Cos here come the bin men!'
The bin tipped upside down and then they caught us by our feet.
He said, 'What a strange creature to meet!'
'Look at that one all slimy and grimy!'
'I like that one so cuddly and soft!'
'Don't be silly the baddest are the best!'
And while they were arguing we slipped away and left,
We ran away home, as frightened as mice,
Just in time for my chicken and rice!

Jenny Czerniakiewicz (10)
Culbokie Primary School, Dingwall

The Ice Skating Princess

Cuddly Crystal had a coo, it always said moo!
She has a house shaped like a heart,
One day she fell out with her friends and now they are apart,
Now that she doesn't have any friends – what will she do?
She lives in the rain so decided to go to Australia in an aeroplane
and never saw her friends again!

Karli Prendergast (7)
Forehill Primary School, Ayr

Emily Love

Emotional Emily is full of jelly
Her sister's name is Kelly
She has lots of shells and bellies
When she is merry she is always on a ferry
She loves Kelly and watching her telly
Her cheeks are rosy and nice and cosy
She doesn't like it when people are nosy.

Chloe McGinnis (7)
Forehill Primary School, Ayr

Beautiful Bella's Umbrella

Beautiful Bella lost her umbrella in a shop one night
It flew back with the wind
She was very happy it was back in sight
One day Beautiful Bella went to a ball
She met a handsome prince who was very tall
One day it was Bella's birthday and she got a pink dress
One night Beautiful Bella went into bed and fell asleep with lots of dreams.

Ava Paterson (7)
Forehill Primary School, Ayr

Pingy Pong's Bin

Pingy Pong plays a song
He plays it in his bin
Pingy Pong bashes hard
He makes a big din
In the bin lived a mouse
He eats cheese and sometimes leaves
Pingy Pong definitely needs a new house
Even though he likes his bin
He really has to move
He enters a dancing competition and showed off his groove
He always wins
The prize was a new house
Just what he needs
But then he starts to miss his huge bin
He started to cry
He quit the dancing competition and said bye bye.

Aodán McGeechan (7)
Forehill Primary School, Ayr

Untitled

Big and scary
Very hairy
Has one eye
Always eats pies
People killer
Has no shower
Tower climber
People miner
You can climb him but there is no point
You'll just fall and break your joint
He is a monster you should know that
Oh I forgot he's also fat.

Jack McKinnon (9)
Forehill Primary School, Ayr

Under The Bed

My house is really haunted
It's scary as can be
There also is a big bee
Teeth like daggers
Toe jagger
I'm not cute
I'm not sweet
I don't get any sleep
I'll hunt you down
I'll crush you down
I'm the worst monster that's lived.

Douglas McKinnon (9)
Forehill Primary School, Ayr

Monster Mania

M ess you up
O nce it sees you, you can't get away
N ever liked anything
S tinks all the time
T his fluffy beast will kill you
E very day he will hunt
R eally strong he is like King Kong

M onsters will hurt you
A nd he will eat your flesh and bones
N ever missed anybody
I diot monster doesn't know how to kill you
A nd all the monsters will kill you
    I sound cruel but what am I? I am a monster.

Cole Love (9)
Forehill Primary School, Ayr

Emily Goes To Spain

Kind Emily goes to Spain
She brings a friend
Who has a big brain
When they got there it was hot
So they sunbathed quite a lot
Then they bought a big house
It was shaped like a crystal
When they got in they sat down and they had a whistle.

Holly Mackie (7)
Forehill Primary School, Ayr

Enormous Emily

When Emily is cheeky she gets a little grumpy
Because she is a greedy girl

She stomps around at the dead of night
Saying, 'Who is a greedy guts, greedy guts, a greedy guts?'

And when the day is done
She sits down and goes to sleep saying, 'Zzzz.'

Lauren Eva Sives (7)
Forehill Primary School, Ayr

Sweet Sweeta

Sweet Sweeta went sky diving
She jumped off a plane and put her parachute on
She could sleep if she wanted

Sweet Sweeta went to the park
She saw a cat purr
Sadly she took the cat back to her owner

Sweet Sweeta is tired
She is going to bed now
Because the day is now done.

Rachael Duffin (7)
Forehill Primary School, Ayr

Pongy Pete

Pongy Pete lives in trash and plays ping pong in the street
When he does, Pete eats meat
In the trash he is very smelly
Because he never washes and he watches too much telly
He has his mouth open at all times
And he is red and black just like a pattern.

Dylan Roberts (7)
Forehill Primary School, Ayr

Vicious Violet

Vicious Violet lived in Egypt
She was only seventeen
She lived inside a pyramid and she kept it nice and clean
She got in a fight with a mummy and pulled his bandages off
The mummy's bandages were so dusty
She could not help her cough
Violet went to the River Nile and she saw a crocodile
She was very scared when she saw his very big smile.

Chloe Greenwood (7)
Forehill Primary School, Ayr

Tornado's Revenge

Tornado lives in a farm
And he does no harm
One day Tornado destroyed another farm
But then the god of the wind came and struck a lightning bolt
And Tornado got destroyed
He never went back to his despicable ways.

Cameron Sym (8)
Forehill Primary School, Ayr

Happy Henry

Please meet my monster Henry
He's the champion of the century
His cheeks are very chubby
His knees are very stubby
He's stinky and he's smelly
He looks likes he's made of jelly
He is old and he can fold
And his medals are made of gold.

Max Mason (7)
Forehill Primary School, Ayr

Smelly Bobby

Glasgow's best monster is Bobby
He has a smelly hobby
We laugh when he walks down the road
He looks funny as well
He is hairy and he spies on people
He is nosy sometimes
He is cosy, he is bigger than his nose
He is good but he's rude
His snot comes out of his nose when it pops.

Lyell King (7)
Forehill Primary School, Ayr

The Night Killer

Soul eater
People stealer
Brain squeezer
Gut taker
Heart taker
Blood sucker
My name's Tuker
I kill people
I will tell you
I'm a monster!

Ryan McGeachin (9)
Forehill Primary School, Ayr

Monster Mania

You better run away
Or I'll break you up like clay
I get you when you're sleeping
I kill you when you're weeping
I'll smash a door
I would fight a boar
I end lives
I cut open with knives
I can bite
And I'll give you a fright
My name is Lobster
Because I'm a monster.

Zack Graham (9)
Forehill Primary School, Ayr

Disaster In The Himalayas

One day in the Himalayas
A person came along
He did a certain action
And it was very wrong
He moved when a monster was looking
It was as scary as a psycho killer
He jumped out of his skin
It was such a thriller
He parachuted north
Yes he is away
Man that was scary
Hip, hip hooray!

Callum Boyd (9)
Forehill Primary School, Ayr

Monster Play

This monster is very scary and hairy
Table hider, they call me Hairy Mary
I am inside everybody's head
They just can't seem to get to bed
They call me Mallow because I love eating lovely jubbly marshmallows
I am a caring but cuckoo creature
I am very tough but I don't have any fluff
I look like a boiled egg
So don't come near me
Or I will bite your leg
I am Mallow
Don't come near me, you will be dead
I warn you!
From Little Fred.

Abbie Boyd (9)
Forehill Primary School, Ayr

The Monster Under My Bed!

Every night I go to bed
I hear the TV going downstairs
So I cuddle up with big, blue ted
I think there is something under my bed
I got up one night and took a peek
I wanted to see what it was
But all I saw was big, chubby cheeks
So I looked away to see if he would come out but he didn't
So eventually he came and and his five eyes were glowing mad
He was colourful and stripy
But he was not bad but very sad
So you may come near him because he is very kind
But just to warn you he has a very weird mind.

Sarah Connell (9)
Forehill Primary School, Ayr

I Love My Medusa Monster

My monster is Medusa
Her news is always filled with extravaganza
She loves her tail, she looks really pale
She is my Medusa monster
She hates her veggies, people give her wedgies
She is my Medusa monster
She wanted to play but she just can't stay
She is my Medusa monster
She's always angry, she just can't get enough
She's like a little cream puff
I love my Medusa monster
She's very hairy, I don't know if she's really scary
and her teeth are like knives
And she can end lives
So I'll stay away until the end of the day
She keeps clean and her age is 15
I love my Medusa monster!

Jenna Currie (9)
Forehill Primary School, Ayr

Monster In The Sea

Monster in sea, as angry as can be
Swimming in the ocean
Not so happy swimming, swimming, swimming when boats come by
They never come back cos he's a life taker not a life saver
Battling, bashing, beating, boring, no sleep, eight feet
In a blink of an eye they're gone for life
Drowning, diving, dread
Bigger than 100 metres
2,000,000 litres
On the sea bed
Living in a sea shed.

Curtis Neave (9)
Forehill Primary School, Ayr

What Kind Of Monster?

Human eater
Furball keeper
Car seater
Heavy sleeper
Hair pleater
Board game cheater
Loves Peter
Long as a metre
Bird tweeter
I am a . . . random monster!

Adam Meek (9)
Forehill Primary School, Ayr

Monster Maker

Take . . .
A sliver of slime
A kindness ray
A fast cloud
The centre of a lime
Eight beady eyes
The hair of the hairiest man
Teeth as pointy as a pin
Add ten ties
Mix it all together
Now you have a kind monster.

Alexander Burns (9)
Forehill Primary School, Ayr

Who Am I?

I'm big and hairy
But sad and scary
I might bite
I will give a fright
At twelve o'clock at night
But I have the right
Because I'm not fluffy
I'm a toughy
Oh and my teeth are like knives
And I end lives
My name is Bobster
And I'm a . . . monster!

Samuel Drummond (9)
Forehill Primary School, Ayr

All The Monsters In The World

Monsters, monsters, lots of monsters
I can name all the monsters
Bed monsters, head monsters and also red monsters
Red as a rose and smell like a germ
All of them in a monster gem
But there aren't only these monsters
There are scary monsters and hairy monsters
Scary like a nightmare and so hairy it might give you a fright
Mad monsters, dad monsters, bad monsters and also glad monsters
All of them are glad anyway
Now I'll tell you the last thing and it's a secret . . .
After all they aren't that scary
They're just really, really hairy
So no need to run but they're still quite dumb.

Brendan Kong (9)
Forehill Primary School, Ayr

What A Monster

If you look at my monster
You will get a fright
He looks like a lobster
And I am telling you he can bite
He does not like the light
And he might have a fight
He is also very naughty and very vaunty
He has a friend called Monty
Monty is hairy but quite wary
Monty is as big as a bus
Oh and did I mention that my monster is freakishly small
And Monty is ginormous, what a monster.

Claudia Coulter (9)
Forehill Primary School, Ayr

Phil The Non-Scary Monster

Yes, when you hear monsters you think scary
But no, some monsters are as sweet as a fairy
It's brilliantly brilliant
That they're not that different
Here's a monster that is called Phil
He works at the market behind the till
One day he went to a monster party
And he was the only one that was, well, farty
Well you know what I mean, explain no time
It's just hard to rhyme
After he came home that night he said, 'Whoo, I got a fright.'

Liam Mackie (9)
Forehill Primary School, Ayr

Scare Me

Big and hairy
Fluffy and scary
And they call me Mary
I have sharp teeth
And I eat leaves
Big massive feet
Dancing to the beat
I may not be smart
But I have a smelly heart
I am not an Oscar
I am not a roaster
I'm a monster!

Niamh McIntosh (9)
Forehill Primary School, Ayr

My Pet Monster

I have a pet monster it is shaped like a cherry
And wanders around the house happy and merry
It is very small and sleeps in the hall
And when it's outdoors it likes to play football
It will go inside and sleep night to day
Then go in its bath and soak its stress away
Have you guessed it, yes it's a monster
He is very friendly and his favourite food is lobster
But that's it
that's all he will ever do
I should go for now he will be chewing my shoe.

Kaitlyn Brown (10)
Forehill Primary School, Ayr

My Monster

My monster is hairy but is not scary
But it is so merry
It is like a bunny
It is so funny
It likes its mummy but it gets no money to get some honey
It likes flying but it is good at crying
But it has to do a lot of drying
Cooking and cleaning, there is no meaning
They do a lot of dreaming, of singing and speaking
And it is spiky as a knife and as soft as a dog.

Brooke Smillie (9)
Forehill Primary School, Ayr

Candy Monster

Candy was a loving monster
Soft like a cloud that is round up high in the sky
No one is like Candy
Other monsters are nasty, yucky, ucky, smelly and nasty
No, Candy is not like them
He is soft, cuddly, round and young
Small like a bunny
We love monsters that are like Candy.

Brooke Cunningham (9)
Forehill Primary School, Ayr

My Monster Rossie

My monster is cute, sweet but very naughty and very hairy
Its teeth are like a knife, it is friendly and likes to make lots of friends
It is as soft as a pillow
It is as cute as a button
It was as young as a baby
She is shy, sleepy and super
She is very wee just like the friend she made
She is nice, I bet you want to meet her
My monster is called Rossie
I love her.

Carla Russell (9)
Forehill Primary School, Ayr

Monster War

M ilitary monsters
O n the sand
N ear the military base
S tupid military monsters
T anks firing at them
E ating people on the sand
R unning away from the army

W inning against the monsters
A gainst the military army
R ipping the monster's skin.

Tyler Aryee (9)
Forehill Primary School, Ayr

Monster Skate!

Once I went to the skate park and saw a big blob at the ramp
I was drinking juice and bit my straw
I went up to see it but it teleported to a different ramp
It started to camp
It was at the bike range
I got a bike and cycled over and it was hairy like a bear
It was scary like a bear.

Rhys Johnston (9)
Forehill Primary School, Ayr

Call Me The . . .

Life saver,
Friend maker
Light giver,
Naughty never
Looks scary,
Looks hairy
Always happy,
Wears a nappy
Never mean,
Lives in a dream
Feels cuddly,
Always muddly
I can be an animal
Or a human or bird
But just for now
I'm a . . . monster.

Lora McNamee (9)
Forehill Primary School, Ayr

My Monster

Milly is really cute even more cute than Sully
Sully is the baby monster and he is really lovely
He dances all day and sleeps all night
And he keeps his teddy with him until light
He doesn't like the heat but he will leave the house to get something to eat
Even though he is cute he can still play the flute
His favourite food is cupcakes.

Shannon McLaughlin (9)
Forehill Primary School, Ayr

Call Of Duty Black Ops II

David the monster was walking one day
Then he met Sevembi
He had his army with him
Then they heard shouting
They grabbed an MK-48 and had a war
They won the war and screamed and shouted
David went into a helicopter
Then they went on a boat
David went with Hudson to save Woods
They opened a big crater
And saw Woods the dafty
And took him to safety.

Ryan Keating (9)
Forehill Primary School, Ayr

The Day I Went To Cobble Wobble

Once upon a time
I ate a juicy lime.
But it didn't taste right
I saw a monster
I said, 'Let's fight!'
He said he didn't want to.
Instead he said, 'Let's go to Cobble Wobble.'
And that's exactly where we went.
He said his name was Freckle
'And after three, say wheeeee!'
'1, 2, 3
Wheeee!'
Cobble Wobble was jelly
I jumped and sunk.
Freckle had to save me
We walked around.
And guess what we found . . . ?
A really juicy lime!

Ninamarie Crossey (9)
Furnace Primary School, Inveraray

Pet Planet

On Pet Planet in the forest
Was this friendly monster called Coco
Coco was sweet and kind
So Coco went out to see if she could make friends
But no one wanted to be friends with her
Then someone came and she made friends
They were playing together.

Samantha Knight (9)
Furnace Primary School, Inveraray

My Pet Fuzzy Albert

Me and my fuzzy fluffy little friend
Thought that we had come to an end
This morning we went for a walk
And had a rather surprising shock
Then something happened,
It happened I swear
Out of a tree there came a brown bear
It had matted brown fur
And to clean its teeth would it ever occur?
It roared at us then started to chase
Oh then we ran at a rather fast pace
Suddenly you heard a loud roar from the distance
Then the bear took a far glance
He went out of sight
And that was the end of a very hard fight.

Mollie Ford (10)
Glencairn Primary School, Stevenston

The Day I Met Ogg

I saw something strange one day at the park
Through fog steaming up I stared at the dark
A monster came out 'Ogg, ogg, ogg!' he said
That must be his name, I was full of dread.
When the fog was clear I saw friendly eyes
Adorable smile, lighting up the skies
From Planet Licous Ogg had travelled far
Zooming round the moon and passed the sparkling star
This tiny monster I wanted as a pet
'Come home with me and you won't regret.'
Excitedly Ogg agreed to come with me
'Can we go to school? A pupil I'll be.'
Miss Gray was in shock when Ogg flew to class
'Don't worry,' I said, 'he's brilliant at maths!'
With me ever since my cute monster friend
I love him so much and that is the end!

Sophie Doherty (10)
Glencairn Primary School, Stevenston

Brian The Monster

I know a monster called Brian
Who never ever stops crying,
And he lives in a small place called Ireland.
He is good and not bad,
But he is very, very sad,
Because he has no friends,
So one day I suggested we go away
To Antarctica the next day,
We packed our bags with hats and scarves
When we got there we saw some polar bears
And penguins sliding on their tummies
We got to their house
And met the penguin's spouse
Then we had some lovely chicken for tea.

Rachel Irvine (11)
Glencairn Primary School, Stevenston

Mr Rainbow Fancy Pants

There was once a bubbly, bouncy creature,
And that was just some of its features
Mr Rainbow Fancy Pants was its name
He is from colourful Crystal Castle
And he dreams of lots of fame.
But one day he fell from his castle in the sky
And fell straight into an ice rink,
Don't ask me why
He sees figure skaters, he feels cold.
He hears music, he says, 'Wow! Look at them.'
It was skates made of gold
He put them on and stepped on the ice
He did a very good spin
He was like a proper figure skater
That spin was very, very nice.

Jhena Dickie (10)
Glencairn Primary School, Stevenston

The Candy Monster

One day a portal opened on my way home
And a small monster appeared and covered me in foam
'Oh sorry I did not mean to!' he said
'I'm from Candy World do you need to be fed?'
'No thank you,' I said, 'maybe later.
I'm off to the rink because I'm a skater'
'Can you do a double toe loop?'
'Yes I can,' he said, 'look there's a hoop!'
We headed home to have our tea
Lots of candy for my monster and me.

Luke Wakenell (10)
Glencairn Primary School, Stevenston

Devil The Monster

My friend Devil is small,
My friend Devil is mean,
My friend Devil lives in a cave,
We go on adventures,
And play with board games,
He's red as a rose,
Smells like a block of old cheese,
Devil is mean to others but not me.
That's why we are monster friends.

Abby Wallace (11)
Glencairn Primary School, Stevenston

Untitled

There is a monster in my house
It makes a lot of noise
There is a monster in my house
He is crazy, wild and annoying
There is a monster in my house
He's scary, short and sneaky

There is a monster in my room
He is as scary as a ghost
There is a monster in my room
Who hides under my bed
There is a monster in my room
He never shows his face

But all along it's just my imagination
The monster is actually me
It's my clone that appears
When I'm asked to do something.

Keirin Bramwell (11)
Glencairn Primary School, Stevenston

Goodbye, Cryptopia

Captain Smuggles is as sweet as a peach
Captain Smuggles likes to eat
He went into his Cryptopian garden
Where he had some tasty treats
He is short and stubby
He is fuzzy and tubby
Then he went to the street
To find something to eat
He found an old spaceship of brass
So he put his face to the glass
He fell with a bang
Then he heard a clang
As he left Cryptopia behind
Little did he know this would be
His final Cryptopian ride.

Paige Simson (11)
Glencairn Primary School, Stevenston

Mr Scary

Mister Scary is gross, fierce and tall
He likes playing with his super ball.
His cave is pitch-black like a blackbird's feather
On his TV he likes watching the weather.
Off he went to swim in the pool
After that he played on a bull.

Ryan Watt (8)
Glencairn Primary School, Stevenston

The Monster Who Saved The World . . .

When I walked home from school
I saw a monster that was cool
He was cuddly and sweet
Spiky head and smelly feet
'Can I be your monster friend?'
'Always, until the very end.'

Ashley Smith (10)
Glencairn Primary School, Stevenston

Cranky

Once I met a monster called Cranky
Lots of people think he's manky
His body is as white as snow
Cranky went to Aberdeen
To meet the monster queen.
On his way he met a snake
The snake really likes to bake
When he got there he said, 'Hello!'
Then someone played the cello.

Jamie Johnson (8)
Glencairn Primary School, Stevenston

Bo

Once I was sitting on my seat
I heard a mysterious beat
I went downstairs and saw a monster
Who was munching on the toaster.
'Oh my name's Bo, I run fast like a tiger
My favourite drink is milk
And I like to eat silk.
I live in a lab in a secret tunnel
Come and see I've got a funnel!'

Gemma Irvine (8)
Glencairn Primary School, Stevenston

Speedo

His name is Speedo and he really likes to run
He also likes to have parties and have some fun
He lives on Planet Gorg which is as blue as the sky
Some of his friends are naughty and lie.
He went outside and saw a sight.
Something that was really bright.
The light blinded all of his friends because it was so light
He zoomed to the back where it was dark as night.
He jumped through the power surge and ripped the circuits out
Then all of his happy friends all gave a shout.

Logan Stoney (8)
Glencairn Primary School, Stevenston

Vamp-Snake

Hey my monster's called Vamp Snake
But seriously it's not like he lives in a lake
His castle's as dark as the darkest night
But don't worry he won't bite
Or ever get caught in a fight
He only comes out at day, not night
And he always does everything right
He only lives around the block
But for some reason he never talks.

Katie Mortimer (8)
Glencairn Primary School, Stevenston

Marvellous Mystery

I was having a walk and I came across a temple
There was something screeching, it sounded mental
I came even closer to the mossy wall
Then I saw a monster having a ball
I shouted, 'Hey what are you named?'
He turned around and looked ashamed
'Don't be sad, come home with me
I will make you a yummy tea.'
We walked through the jungle, he was scared
'It's OK,' I said, 'we're both paired.'
Then we got home and opened the door
We put on the TV and looked at the football score
We ran up the stairs like two grizzly bears
He slept in my bed like no one cares!

Matthew Boyd (11)
Glencairn Primary School, Stevenston

Gobble

Once there was a monster called Gobble and he was scary
He lived in Rubble Bubble Loby Woby Slopy and he was hairy
Gobble's most favourite food was a car.
Every so often he liked to go to a bar.
Gobble decided to go to the shops to buy a cake
Then he strolled down to the lake.

Raymond McLaughlin (8)
Glencairn Primary School, Stevenston

Baby Kayday

I was walking along one sunny day
It was as cool as being near a bay
Suddenly, I heard people shout, 'Run!'
I looked up at the sky and heard the shot of a gun
A tiny blanket was falling from the sky
I looked left and right, I thought I was going to die
Goodness me, it's an alien but a baby
I'm going to keep it and I'll called it Baby Kayday
We laughed, she's so cute and funny
But then came Baby Kayday's parents wanting their honey
They took her home, what a shame
But I remembered this is only a video game!

Rebecca Baird (10)
Glencairn Primary School, Stevenston

The Surprise

At the park I was watching the birds on the tree
Then I smelt some smoke coming from behind me
I looked over and I saw no light
Suddenly, something popped out and gave me a fright
It was cute, loveable like a small toy
I think it was probably the size of a little boy
That day I asked him, 'Hey what's your name?'
He never replied because that was his game
I walked closer and heard him cry
I looked at his face and asked him why?
All he said was his name is Boggle
His own ship was called The Toggle
I asked him, 'Come home with me?'
He replied, 'Only if I don't have to pay a fee.'

Hollie McGinn
Glencairn Primary School, Stevenston

James' Monsters

Monsters leave poo or goo wherever they walk
oh I wish they could talk.
They give you frights at night
but they can't fight.
Monsters can't give you a scare
if you are aware.
Monsters are revolting
but they will send you bolting.
Monsters are scary, go away or
you will pay so just go away.
They like scaring at Perth
but they're dominating Earth.
There are bad and good monsters
but the bad could turn good
or starve them of food.
That would be very mean
but I am quite keen.
I wonder if there is a monster planet
because I would ban it.
Now they are all good and not rude
that means they are all cool dudes!

James McNeil
Greenview Special School, Glasgow

Evil Evan

Evil Evan was on a trip to see his family
When he was on the spaceship he was so happy
The spaceship crashed and landed on Mars.
He got out and said, 'Where are all the cars?'
He found a map on the floor
It looks like a bit of a bore.
He followed it to see what it's like.
But later on he found a bike.
He found an X that looked like the one on the map
Evil Evan dug it up and asked, 'What's that?'
He heard a voice that said, 'Dig it up, it's treasure!'
Evil Evan shouted back, 'With pleasure!'
So he opened it and saw gold and diamonds
Then he suddenly got very old
He saw a spaceship and they had fish and chips
They came and picked him up and they grabbed everything
They took off and went back to Lava Land and they were rich.

Aidan Shaw (10)
Halfmerke Primary School, East Kilbride

Slimy Scully

Slimy Scully came up from Atlantis
He came up from the sea to surprise us.
He told us he would protect us
From the evil, echoing volcano people.

But the bad guys had already started
And I had started crying into Marty.
They had taken over the USA
So I dialled for the CIA

Slimy Scully creates a tsunami
That wipes them into the sky
As we all cheered when he began to fly
I shouted out, 'Are you intelligent, are you courageous?'
He said, 'I may be small, I may be a fish but I am ferocious.'

Connor Pollock (10)
Halfmerke Primary School, East Kilbride

Flonke The Monster

I was woken up by a knock at the door
I ran and got my slippers that were on the floor
'Hello!' said a pink creature
Who is that? I thought.
Is it my new heater?
'I'm Flonke!' he mumbled
And then his tummy rumbled.

I looked at him head to toe
'Oh my goodness I need to go!'
'Wait!' he shouted as I bolted
He grabbed me by the arm.
'Go away you could harm!'
He looked quite dangerous.
He had a garden on his head,
Converse that were red,
Two big long ears
And looked about twelve years.

'So, Charlie, we are going to go on an adventure
I hope we will find some treasure!'

In Cornwall, we sat by the beach
And had five ice creams each!
And in London I bought a camera to take
Pictures of landmarks including Flonke
Standing beside a huge banana.
Last was Edinburgh
It was OK until we went to a ceilidh
Flonke couldn't dance at all
People stared at us in the hall
Then we came to the end of our trip
'Bye!' I said with a tear in my eye.
'Bye, Charlie!' Flonke said like he was about to cry
He clicked his fingers and off he went
And . . . I guess that's the end!

Katie Smith (10)
Halfmerke Primary School, East Kilbride

Lonely Monster

One day I went to school to try to get friends
But when I went they all sent out a loud shout
So later that day I went home to say
'Mum I hope I have a friend from another planet some day!'
Then one day I went to find a monster who was nice and kind.
I was blind at the time to not find a new friend
There was one at the shop about to buy a cold pop.
He was six feet three, just the same size as me
I asked him, 'Do you want to play hide-and-seek?'
He said, 'Yes, I'll be it'
But every time he seeks
He always peeks
To see where you are.
After that we were done
After all that fun
Then I went to bed
To rest my sleepy head.

Brian Robertson (10)
Halfmerke Primary School, East Kilbride

Bluey Ballerina

The town of Monsteretta was doing just fine
Until a flash of light
Out came Daniel,
He must have got a fright.
The first person to talk to him was Bluey Ballerina
Her real name was Tina.
'Where are you from?' she exclaimed quite eerie!
'Earth, where am I here?'
'Monsteretta, I will try and help you get home.'
'Let's go to a laboratory.'
'Before we go let's grab a quick kebab.'
At the laboratory they zapped and zipped until *bam!*
They were in a jungle.
They had to find their way to the magic temple of X-ar
There was one problem
There was a huge dam.
'We're not passing it today!' exclaimed Daniel.
They found temples, wild animals and had to eat bugs.
They wished for a jar of cookies and a glass of water.
But sadly they were looking for the temple of X-ar
When they found it they got back home. Yippee!

Ciara Young (10)
Halfmerke Primary School, East Kilbride

Friendly Fred

I was walking down the beach
And I got a freaky feeling
I heard something
I turned round to see
A friendly, fuzzy, furry monster following me.
I got a fright
I got a shock
I ran away like a shot.

Then I realised he's cute as a button
And a loveable thing.
So I asked why he was following me
He said he wanted to be friends with me
We had a ball
We had a laugh
I had great fun today.
I hope he comes another day.

Iona McDougall (10)
Halfmerke Primary School, East Kilbride

Pongy Pete

Pongy Pete got out of his can
That was smelly all round
He went to the park
Sat on a bench, sent all the little monsters crying to bed.
A little creature called Fuzzy Buzzy came over
'I'm a NSPCM lady and I am here to help you,' she squeaked holding her nose.
'Yessss!' replied Peter holding a pose.
So Fuzzy Buzzy got clear water and non-rotten food for Pete.
They brushed his hair got all the rotten fish out.
Scratch! Ooze! Glob!
The lady said, 'Bath time!'
They got him in the bath.
The water was all green.
They rubbed and scrubbed and got him clean.
The whole world called him Pretty Pete
He was as handsome as Prince Charming.

Cairnie Glaister (10)
Halfmerke Primary School, East Kilbride

64

Plan To Take Over The World

On my way home from football
Something grabbed me and it was huge.
It had rough skin and was as strong as an ox.
His arms were hairy just like a fox.
I looked at his face, he was ugly.
He was as hot as lava
But we were going so fast I did not feel it.
When we got to the centre of the Earth
His friends Bleep and Bloob told me
I had to help them take over Perth.
I was scared I would get burned by lava
I saw an exit and I said, 'Sayonara!'
They chased me but I locked the door
I trapped them in a hole under the floor.

Jackson Leishman (10)
Halfmerke Primary School, East Kilbride

The Journey

I came back from Tokyo
With Evil Evan and Big Bad Barry
We went to the beach and I had a fall
Then we played volleyball.
We had to leave for Euro Gamer
But we were much lamer than being a gamer
When we arrived we played some games
There were some pains in the games.
We met some awesome monster tubers
Called Symdieater and Vanman
We ran all the way back from Euro Gamer
Daft Danny ran as fast as Mo Farah.
When Daft Danny got back he dived into bed.
He was sound asleep like he was dead.

Lewis Borthwick (10)
Halfmerke Primary School, East Kilbride

Friendly Fuzz

'Mum there's a monster under my bed
And he's all big and red
But he looks very friendly
Because he's just been fed
He likes to eat spiders' webs
But he only eats them
From under beds.'

'Oh stop talking rubbish!
I heard what you said,
There are no monsters under any bed!'

'No Mum there is, there definitely is
And he's trying give the dog
A great big kiss!'

'I suppose he's raiding the cupboard
For a packet of crisps!'

'In fact he is!
And he's still trying to give the dog
A great big kiss!'

Rachel Green (10)
Halfmerke Primary School, East Kilbride

Help Find A Friend

A monster you might have heard of
He is called Fuzzy Frank
He is as loud as a volcano
And as big as a tank.

He is green and blue, hairy too
Fuzzy Frank likes to wear a hat
And has one shoe
He is funny and depressed.

Fuzzy Frank has no friends
So he decided to go and find a friend
He jumped on a plane
And went to Spain
But it crashed on Earth.

That's when I met Fuzzy Frank
'Hello what's your name?' I said.
'Fuzzy Frank nice to meet you
Can you help me, I'm only two?'
'OK but where are you from?'
'I'm from Monster Japan on Mars.'

We went to Mars and we had a lot of fun
Fuzzy Frank did find a friend
And they moved to the sun.

Jennifer Marshall (10)
Halfmerke Primary School, East Kilbride

Peek At The Mall

Peek was sitting on her chair
Looking as cute as a button
She wanted to go on her spaceship
So off she went.

She cried, 'Kapoot!'
She fell onto Orla's chute
Up jumped Orla, she got a fright.
Banging at the window
Where there was light.
'Come in,' yelled Orla
In the dead of night
Peek woke up the very next day
'Let's have pancakes for breakfast
Hip, hip, hooray!'
'Let's go to the mall,' called Orla.
'Wait I need my new shawl.'
They went to Lush
Where she got a blush.
Also to Primark, Next and Nando's
Yum but she overloaded her tum.
They had fun.
'See you soon, miss you already!'
She gave Peek a hug
And off she went up to the sun.

Orla McHugh (10)
Halfmerke Primary School, East Kilbride

Blue Bunny Bella

As I was walking home from school,
I saw this pie,
Drop from the sky
There was a creature eating the pie
I picked it up,
A little friendly blue bunny asked,' What is your name?'
I replied, 'Oh my, my name is Beth
Let's go on an adventure.'
'OK, let's go now, my name is Blue Bunny Bella.'
First we went to my school
Bella said it looked cool
Then we went to Mars to see her school
It had a pool
We came back from Mars
We went to my house to see my toy.
Bella called it a fool.
I asked her, 'Will you come to visit me?'
She said, 'No, why? I am staying here!'
'Let's make you a house,' I said
With a bit of fear.
We then made her a house
She was all warm and comfortable in her house
She was as cute as a button
I hope she comes back soon
She said she would.

Emma Scott (10)
Halfmerke Primary School, East Kilbride

Podd

A boy called Ciaran was walking to school
When a monster said, 'You look pretty cool!
I'm Podd, nice to meet you.'
'Hi, I'm Ciaran, you look cool too!'
He had red curly yellow teeth too
He said, 'Do you want to go to the moon
To see my kind?'
'Are you blind?'
Podd replied, 'Enough talk let's walk.'
'How are we going to get to the moon?'
'In my spaceship of course.'
When we got on
He offered me cheese
I said, 'Yes please.'
We landed with a crash and a bang
I met Podd's mum who was fat
And always wore a hat.
Then I heard footsteps like thunder.
I got a bit scared but it was just Podd's dad
The king of the moon
He offered to show me around.
I said, 'I can't, I need to go.'
So Podd flew me back to school
And I was left feeling really cool.

Ciaran McClure (10)
Halfmerke Primary School, East Kilbride

Fish Spot

I wis swimming in the Scottish sea
I saw a creature with broon hair and red skin
Like blood with blue spots
I swam to the monster in the sea
I had a big breath
I swam reet doon to the bottom of the sea
The monster said, 'Come with me.'
I saw seaweed waving on the surface
Efficient fishes of all shapes and sizes
Were wiggling like worms
I am as soggy as a sponge
I want to go home
'Goodbye Fish Spot.'

Archie Wilson (10)
Insch School, Insch

Colin

One day I was at the cinema
Watching a horror movie
A monster jumped out of the screen!
He was friendly so he told me his name
He called himself Colin

His home planet is Mars
After I met him
We went to the park
We played
Then I showed him around my house
Then we got food and water all at Asda.

Dylan Craig (9)
Insch School, Insch

The Blob

I was walking from school
When I saw a little blob
We chatted for a wee bit
And he said his name was Bob
His belly started to rumble
And he said, 'You'd better start to run!'
What did he mean?
Maybe I was done.
His jaws began to squidge
He opened his enormous mouth
And gave a roar so loud
It could be heard from the south.
I ran into the woods
And tripped over a slippery, smooth log
But before Bob could get me
He was attacked by a fierce wild dog!
Little did I know that
When I was in my bed at night
He was waiting at my window,
Ready to give me a fright!

Ben Forsyth (10)
Insch School, Insch

Herm The Worm

Did I ever tell you about the time I went to Planet Germ?
I met a chap as green as grass
His name was Herm the Worm
He was sad because his friends were being mean
I asked him, 'Why?'
He said because he was never to be seen
So I tried my very hardest to try to cheer him up
But all was in vain,
Especially when I showed him how to keepie-up
We decided to play a game of hide-and-seek
'I'll count,' Herm said,
And I told him not to peek!
There I was looking for a place to hide
Then I saw a shack as old as day,
And I crept inside . . .
Herm the Worm got tired and decided to have a nap
But then a sudden thought struck,
I will ask to be his chap
So he found me and asked to be my friend
I said, 'Yes of course.'
And I hope that we stay this way till the very end.

Charlotte Comber (10)
Insch School, Insch

The Superhero!

One day I went to school
My school is big as an elephant
My mother says that I have to go to school
In the school there was a little mouse.

In the school I met my brothers
Harry, Spiky and Mike
They are like mice but they are evil
So I tried to save the world.

Now let's enjoy school but the fun is not starting
But now the school is epic
Lump my friend came home
And he wanted to save the world with me
And we did save the world . . .

Freya Ogilvie (9)
Insch School, Insch

Evil

One day in America
A monster called Evil Load
Was walking down the road

He saw two mysterious men
Robbing a bank
Evil activated a device then they sank

Last week someone had a bomb
He activated it in someone's house
There are three hostages and one mouse

It planted another device then
It stopped the bomb and the killer
Even one of them was called Ann Miller.

Harry Macduff (9)
Insch School, Insch

Cheese Sandwiches

When I was walking home from school
I saw nine monsters all big and blue
They all had one leg each, enchanting eyes
And tails like curly fries.

He offered me a sandwich of cheese
'Take one,' he said, 'take one please.'
I took a sandwich, it was yum.
He wanted to make more to fill people's tum.

We set up a stall in the park
A man called Mark
Who was riding on a bike of bark
Bought a sandwich and said it was yum.
And would definitely fill people's tum
We started a business called Monkey and Me!

Eve Fraser (10)
Insch School, Insch

The Armed Fire Bolt

I made a monster that got out of control
He called himself Rat Bat,
He hurt lots of people
He was as mean as a dark dragon
His fire bolts were as dangerous as lava
He flew around town
Attacking houses and fields
On top of a magic mountain he stepped
He looked at what he had done
He was shocked at what he did.
After that when anything bad happened
Rat Bat helped
And then the people made more armed fire bolts.

David McLeod (9)
Insch School, Insch

Evil Or Not

One day I met a monster
With teeth as sharp as knives
Her hair as yellow as gold
Her tongue is a pickaxe as strong as steel
Her body as hot as lava, one touch and you'd be dead
She had two mouths, one for sucking the blood out your body
The other for eating your bed
Her hands were double-headed snakes
With venom as strong as black mambas
And was as hot as fire
Her body was a cloud, as light as a feather
And her eyes were as blue as the ocean
Although she sounds scary, she is as nice as a snail
I'd like to tell you all the adventures we've been on
But I would run out of space.
And that's why I'll tell you just one
It was a dark day with nothing to see
Except the simmering light from my house
Me, my mum, my sister and dad were all out in the garden
Waiting to see a shining light
A sign of my monster's return
Mum said in the morning we'd go to the café
Then the park to play
And when she arrived we did exactly that
When we got to the café we all had hot chocolate
Except my monster who had 93
When we got to the park
We played on the swings, slide, roundabout and everything else
When we got home we ate tea
Brushed our teeth and went to bed.

Emily McGlashan (8)
Insch School, Insch

The Green And Red Monster

I met him at Tesco.
He had nails as sharp as knives
Ears as pointy as needles
He is round as a ghost
And is as loud as a werewolf
We bought oil for the robot party
He invited all his friends
They made such a big noise
As loud as a gunshot
Someone called the robot police
The police arrested Willy
For making too much noise
His friends ran away
So the police put Willy in jail
It cost his friends 1,000 robot coins
To get him out again.
When Willy got out of jail
He went to Tesco with Ben
And bought some oil
Willy went back to his apartment
And drank the dark juicy oil
But it made him come up in boils
So he decided to fly to the moon.
Willy met aliens that tried to kill him
But Willy just beat them up
Willy stole 10,000 robot coins from the boss
The boss tried to find him but he was lost.

Hugo Ricketts (10)
Insch School, Insch

I Hate Spiders!

Me and Tweetie lived in Egypt
I am a blue jelly blob
I am about as big as a dog
Tweetie is a petite, green bird
He was as small as three rats

We wanted to see the pyramids
Me and my companion strolled to one of the openings
That pyramid was as big as two elephants
There was a sign outside that read *Danger!*
But we took no notice.

The sign was as big as a water bottle
So we went in
The passageway was covered in spiderwebs
Soon I got to the door and it looked even scarier
Then I peeked round the door

It was Tweetie
But he had eight legs
And pure white fangs
He had transformed into a spider
But not just any spider, he was Spideruss.

Spideruss possessed Tweetie
He was as scary as a horror movie
He was our worst enemy (he hated us)
Spideruss wanted to rule all creatures and be king
But it was easy to stop him.

He had a shaggy brown coat
And glaring red eyes
But I knew his weakness
It was water, he hated it
After his cousin Incy got washed down the drain.

But just then I saw a water pipe
So I pulled it
And covered him in water
The water was as cold as ice
Spideruss started to hiss and just then he vanished.

Green feathers started to appear
Tweetie was back!
He was sat there mind-blown from the situation
After a day or two he felt much better
Soon we were off on another adventure.

Aimee Duguid (10)
Insch School, Insch

Trob

I met Trob
He was fat as a blob
And as ugly as a slob
He even named his pet Rob
And he would use a stick to prod you.

He was as sneaky as a spy
And he would try to eat your eye
But he wouldn't eat me

Trob went and got us an ice cream
He came back as slow as a turtle
But wait what's that? Is it a foot?

So we strolled back to my house
I felt him breathe in my face
Aww he has breath like a troll!

But when we sat down
I felt like I was being sucked
Then I realised . . .

Josh Cannell (10)
Insch School, Insch

Monster Holiday

One morning I got on the plane
And flew to sunny Spain
But the plane got delayed
Because of a monster
'A monster!' I shouted
It jumped on the plane
And the plane wiggled like a snake
And it shook like a washing machine
We crashed in the middle of France
Through the town we danced and pranced
The day after we went bungee jumping
With Glump Glump, a monster
That is as spiky as a hedgehog
And as sticky as glue
And he will really love you.

Molly Underwood (9)
Insch School, Insch

Afro Hero

One day I went to school
I heard a big crash
What I saw there was cool!

It was a magnificent monster
He had a beard
With legs like a skeleton

We went to the windy trees
And built an enormous tree house
Afro Hero decided to eat some cheese.

Afro Hero thinks he should have a haircut
He wanted a happy look when we came to the haircutter's
The fat man was scared of Afro Hero
I paid for Afro Hero's hair cut
Therefore Afro Hero thought his haircut was good
And after that he went home.

Tom Kolsch (9)
Insch School, Insch

One Dark Night

One dark night I got a really big fright
As a weird flash formed around me.
I thought it was a ghost
Surrounding me by the lamppost

But it wasn't, it was a *monster!*
He called himself Nark
As he faced the pitch-black park.
He was smaller than small
Tinier than a bouncy ball
I told him, 'Let's go home!'
So we did.

Luke Godwin (9)
Insch School, Insch

The Big Mazukia Monster

Mazukia's funny favourite day is today
This fantastic month is May
Today is windy Wednesday
But he cares for each and every brilliant day
He has a noisy piano and he is so fat
He could play with his toes
He has loud drums and he also loves plums
On wonderful Wednesday he has swimming and enjoys playing
On Thursdays he has violin and he loves staring at a boring old pylon
It was sadly time to say goodbye and I started to dramatically cry!

Lois Taylor (8)
Milton Of Leys Primary School, Inverness

A Day Outside

One glorious school day
I walked down the hill
A weird curious monster appeared
From the greenish bushes.
I nearly jumped out of my skin.
The weird-looking monster had a black cape
And shoes as blue as the sea
It had pointy ears like knives
And he is really black like the dark sky.
He said he had to go to his own planet
His name was Sergio Biscuits.

Jack Hamilton (9)
Milton Of Leys Primary School, Inverness

Baby Boo Comes To The Rescue

I was running home determinedly from school
And I encountered a curious creature
We found him swimming slowly in a deep pool
With a very unusual funny fantastic feature
I accidentally asked him his name
And it was apparently Baby Boo.
Baby Boo shouted, 'I'm building a running rocket.
Someday, sometime I will save my playing planet
Have you met my quid queen?
Her name is Jumping Janet.
Are you ready for a rough rocket ride?'
We trailed off through space at the speed of light
Baby Boo found a dragon dancing daringly down the hill
That dragon was trying to take over our wonderful world
Baby Boo bounced bigger than the Empire State Building
Baby Boo killed the dragon with a pun
He was thanked by everyone and finally there was the sun
Baby Boo begged for an award or even a sword
So he became the longest lasting lord.

Kirsten McKay (9)
Milton Of Leys Primary School, Inverness

Mr Fluffy Comes To Town

It was a nice wonderful sunny day.
As I went into the mall
I caught a marvellous monster
The marvellous monster's name was Mr Fluffy
Mr Fluffy was extra cute because he was fluffy
'Mr Fluffy,' I said, 'do you want lunch?'
After I asked he shouted, 'Yes please!'
Then I took Mr Fluffy for some beautiful lunch.
After lunch I said, 'Do you want to come home?'
'OK.'
Mr Fluffy came home with me.
Mr Fluffy climbed into bed. Zzzzz
In the morning Mr Fluffy spotted zebras.
The zebras were sleeping too. Zzzzz
We went into town again.
We had so much fun together
Mr Fluffy was so, so happy, ha, ha, ha!
Me and Mr Fluffy started to laugh.

Gemma Birnie (9)
Milton Of Leys Primary School, Inverness

Flupper And Me

Flupper's favourite day is today.
He likes the day in May.
He plays a magnificent chanter
And enjoys lots of banter
He loves Taylor Swift.
He has been to every concert.
He does not look at any singer.
He went for lunch with Miley Cyrus.
He asked Miley Cyrus,
'Can you say red lorry, yellow lorry?'
She said, 'Yes!'
She sang, 'Red lorry, yellow lorry, red lorry!'
He loves sweets.
And he loves to keep the beat.

Logan Ross (9)
Milton Of Leys Primary School, Inverness

Four Bodied Lives With Me

On the way to work I saw a nice tall monster
I said, 'Hello,'
I said, 'Hello!'
Then he heard me.
We walked to work together
Then we walked to my house
We sang a song called 'Rock and Roll'
'Rock and roll, rock and roll, rock, rock, rock, rock every day.'
This monster had four legs, four arms, eight spikes,
Four heads, one body and four missile launchers.
I asked the monster, 'Would you like to stay here?'
The monster said, 'I would love to stay here!'

Nilavan Tamijmarane (8)
Milton Of Leys Primary School, Inverness

Mr Fuzzball

I was excited because it was the first term at super Sunday school.
I was in Primary One.
There was a soft sunny swimming pool
My nursery project was done.
When I went in the big brown building.
There was my teacher Mr Fuzzball.
Somebody in my class was fidgeting furiously.
Mr Fuzzball picked up the purple phone because there was a call.
When the call was over he told everyone to go outside except me.
Mr Fuzzball was as bright as the sun.
We went to the terrific park and said,
'He is not actually a teacher.'
He said he's from Mars and has no friends.
He said he's very good and said, 'Nice to meet you!'
He said, 'I want some wonderful water to take home to my weird Mars,
That's as cold as an ice cube!'

Liam Moodie (9)
Milton Of Leys Primary School, Inverness

The Great Royal Mrs Fuzzy Pants

Mrs Fuzzy Pants loves to go on walks
Mrs Fuzzy Pants always furiously talks
She is very royal and all she totally loves is myrrh
She has very super soft silky fur
Her family are from the weirdest planet ever – Jupiter!
Maybe that's why they are more stupider
But then she was amazingly kidnapped
She wants to call her pancakes Pidmapped
She met me meeting Max
I said, 'Hey'
And she said, 'Nay.'
She cares for her family
Although they are quite manly
They sing their song,
'Which watch, which watch, with what, witch,' they sang.

Amy Skeoch (9)
Milton Of Leys Primary School, Inverness

Jimmy Rocks Day At London

Jimmy had a favourite fabulous funny day,
His favourite fabulous funny day started in May.
He had a magical marvellous friend called Jack.
That sat on Jimmy's warm weary back.
They started running weirdly around the town.
Going up and down looking for a clown.
Then they visited the gigantic London Eye.
Then Jimmy was a little bit shy, but why?
Then they found the Queen with some ice cream.
Eventually they started staring at Princess Eugene
She asked them in for a cup of tea.
After that they were looking at the bright blue sea.
Then they went to the park.
Then a wild, creepy, frightful brown dog barked at me.
It was Friday finally, at last!
Then started watching a movie
I saw the cast.

Darren Calder (9)
Milton Of Leys Primary School, Inverness

Tiote Takes Over Earth

Tiote lives on Mars
He wants to take over Earth!
He has a brother called Check
His brother has a ship called the Corater Ship!
The ship had three power guns!
The power gun shot up to a billion metres long.
His brother went to sleep. Zzzz!
Tiote went on Check's ship!
He went to the edge of the Earth and shot the gun.
Bang!
There was no humans on Earth anymore!
Well Tiote though they were dead . . .
But they were underground!
The humans made a new gun called the 'Blaster'
They shot the gun. *Bang!*
The aliens were blasted back to Mars.

Tyler Clare (8)
Milton Of Leys Primary School, Inverness

Jim Bob Went To Town And Met The Queen

Jim Bob meets this stunning girl.
He takes her hand and gives her a twirl
'Oh that's my favourite sweet, a Twirl.'
'I know you are very sweet!'
'Oh thank you, you have very nice feet!'
'Oh don't mention it.'
'OK do you want to go for some lovely lunch?'
'It's OK I just had a lot of mini morning maximiser.'
'Well meet me here tomorrow.'
'Deal. Right here, promise I'll be right here.'

'Hi I am here!' said the lady (the Queen)
Jim Bob arrives with a swagger.
He thinks he's got the moves like Jagger
'Oh dear, oh no, I don't think so.'

Luke Seago (9)
Milton Of Leys Primary School, Inverness

Fluff-Bug's Adventure

I encountered an interactive and courageous monster
She had a favourite day
Her favourite day is a sunny Saturday.
On Saturday she went on her blood-red bike.
She stopped at some traffic lights.
Her face went as white as a ghost!
She stopped at a bright pink shop.
The shop was called the Light Lollipop Shop
She went in to buy a lovely lollipop
The lollipop was her favourite colour, glitzy blue
Then she trotted along the deep dark street.
And when she got home she went to sleep!

Maddison Cameron (9)
Milton Of Leys Primary School, Inverness

Our Next Door Neighbour

Our next door neighbour has jet black eyes,
Our next door neighbour likes eating pies!
When he strokes cats they always purr
Oh did I forget to tell you he's a monster?
He woke one morning and ran down the street,,
Looking for beer, there was no one to greet.
He went into town and saw a big limousine
For standing in front of him was Her Majesty the Queen.
What was she thinking? Nobody knows!
For then Her Highness started to glow
It must have been something she had for lunch
She said, 'Sorry, I had a light bulb for brunch!'

Joe Dickinson (9)
Milton Of Leys Primary School, Inverness

Mr Fuzzy

I was wonderfully walking to scary serious school.
I saw a big fluffy fuzzy ball running around the street
It was pink with bright white feet
He told me his name, it was Mr Fuzzy
So I skipped scary, serious school that day
So I took him to my house and sat on some hay.
So I asked if he would like a cup of terrific tea?
He said, 'Yes please!'
While we drank our terrific tea
We listened to the sound of the super sunny sea.
Mr Fuzzy would probably have got tired that day
So he jumped into his awesome big brown bed and . . .
The next morning I woke up suddenly
He shouted, 'Bye, bye,
I will see you tomorrow or go to Skye!'

Rachel Bailey (9)
Milton Of Leys Primary School, Inverness

My Footballing Monster

One day a monster fell from the sky.
I asked him what happened and he didn't lie
His skin is sky blue
And his outfit was the colour of grass
His shoes are as red as blood
And he's extremely fit.

His name was Footie,
And he liked a Tuttie Fruitie
He said, 'I want to play for a football club
But my teammates kicked me out.'

He asked if we could start a super street team
I told my friends and they said it was extreme.
We had a game against dreaded Greenwood,
I was so tense until we got a penalty.

Footie took it, he scored a goal, I asked,
'Have you been good since you were young?'
And he said, 'Yes, I'm very good.'
'Well you were very good against Greenwood.'
And that's my strong, sensible Footie.

William Urquhart (9)
Milton Of Leys Primary School, Inverness

Me And My Monster

I met a monster in the school
In a cupboard looking cool
I asked its name twice
It said something so quiet like mice
It was big, blue and fluffy
With a top hat and a bruise
I asked it its name once more
It sounded like Broozer

So me and Broozer went to class
To do a little bit of maths
After that we went back home
And played a game of tig alone
Broozer saw my mother
Then he eyed my brother
'Argh!' my brother howled like a wolf
Oh no he bit my brother's finger off!

We left home very fast
And got to the park at last
We played on the slippery slide
My monster stood up with pride
He smiled and said, 'I really must go'
So he clicked his finger, tapped his toe
And *poof* he was gone!
Phew! I hope I am not in terrible trouble!

Sharleen Kennedy (9)
Milton Of Leys Primary School, Inverness

Me And My Monster Fluffy!

One day I was at school
I saw something vicious but also cute
She is as yellow as a buttercup
That is my monster Fluffy.

After you get to know her
She stopped being vicious
I took her to the theme park
Which was just like a play park
We went on the water slide
Which was so hilarious
We went on lots of cool rides.

The next day
Fluffy the fuzzy monster
Had to go home
Me and my monster Fluffy!
I said, 'Will you visit me?'
'Yes,' said the fluffy fuzzy monster.

Naomi Stewart (9)
Milton Of Leys Primary School, Inverness

My Monster And Me

I met my monster in Paris,
A theatre I was at,
Singing a little song,
But then I smelt a pongy pong
Backstage in the closet I went . . .

'My name is Spot!' said the monster,
'Hi!' I said,
He came out of the closet
He was as orange as a tangerine
'My nickname is Purple Ding Dong.'

We went to X Factor
We did some acrobatics
Then some aquatics
We won £1 million.

I felt like I was dreaming
I heard Spot weeping
But it was with joy.

We had to say goodbye
I was very upset
I gave him money
I saw him coming out of the store
But he came out with apple and apricot alcohol.

Beth Mackenzie (10)
Milton Of Leys Primary School, Inverness

The Best Day Ever With A Monster

One day I was at school
People were trying to act cool
I found my vicious monster in my school bag
But it's so cute and it had a suit.
My monster is magic and full of the cuddles
And it also stands in puddles.

It nearly jumped into the class
But it was fiddling with glass.
Fuzzy looks like a tiny teddy bear.
I snatched the glass off her but she started to roar.
We started to play, it was the best day
In the whole entire world.
She said, 'Now I really must go.'
I said, 'goodbye and thank you so much for
The fabulous, funny and vast amount of time
It has come to an end but you will come again right?'
There was no reply but then it was time to go.
We said goodbye cheerfully with a bit of a cry
Bye, bye to the best monster in the world
See you next time Fuzzy!

Leah Hollister (9)
Milton Of Leys Primary School, Inverness

Me And Toastie's Great Adventure To School

I'm making my toast in the morning
When there appears a monster
It gives me a shock, it gives me a scare
But I take it upstairs.

I try to show my brother
But he didn't like him at all
Then he said, 'Let's go to the mall'
So I said, 'Not at all, I have to go to school.'

I took him to school, he sat on my chair,
My friend Jonny said he was as cute as a bear,
As hot as an oven
And as funny as a clown.

My teacher wobbled in
She gave me a scary stare
Toastie did not like her at all
So he jumped on her and gave her a scare
She sent us home
So home we went.

Freya MacLennan (10)
Milton Of Leys Primary School, Inverness

Me And My Monster!

I have a monster called Cuddles
She loves to jump in muddy puddles
I found her in my class
She was fiddling with some glass
I took it from her quickly and she began to roar
It was so very loud that I too wanted to roar
But I knew if I did that she would be scared
And to upset my monster I would not have dared
I took my monster home and let her play with glass
And after that I had to go back to class
Me and my monster said, 'Bye, bye.'

Emily Willox (9)
Milton Of Leys Primary School, Inverness

The Day The Underworld Ends!

I open my jar of jelly
And out pops a monster with a blue tie
He has an enormous round belly
He always tells lies
His name is Frank
He likes doing pranks
He eats planks
And he likes changing his pants
We go to the underworld and meet friends
We go to the castle, we have some fun
A big vicious dragon came out
Frank decided to run
We destroy the underworld with a twirl.

Robbie Fraser (9)
Milton Of Leys Primary School, Inverness

My Monster Poem

I met my blue buddy
Inside the school study
He was funny, he was cool
He had a nice home too.
A roof over his head
And a very comfy bed.
So I took him home to my bed
So we played instead
He told me why he left his home
The story was scary, ferocious too.
He asked me to go with him to Las Vegas
It was fun, it was scary
Lots of people were hairy!
So we went home before it was too late
We have to say goodbye to my mate.

Kieran Watson (9)
Milton Of Leys Primary School, Inverness

Unisaurus' End

The thing fell from the sky
Almost squished me alive
It was as ugly as a troll
I asked, 'What's your name?'
He said, 'Unisaurus.'

Man that name creeped me out
Then my mum came out
How do I hide something
Bigger than a monster truck?

We went to town
Big mistake!
He ate the whole town
Including me!
Found his core
Stabbed it with a pointy pencil
That's the end of Unisaurus!

Jonathan Williams (10)
Milton Of Leys Primary School, Inverness

A Day With A Monster

I have just found a monster in my tray
It has been hiding behind some modelling clay
I took it out and we started to play
We even played with the modelling clay.

Finlay the purple furred monster
Made a clay tray
He made a carrot
He even made a little pink parrot
But then he got hungry and started to roar
And before you knew it he had eaten the classroom floor

He sat on my lap and started to cry
Then sadly said, 'Bye, bye'
Hopped into my tray and went away
And the comfy classroom floor came back again.

Gabrielle MacDonald (9)
Milton Of Leys Primary School, Inverness

Fuzz The Monster

As I was snoozing, I heard a bouncy noise.
It came from under my bed!
So I looked to see what the matter was
And there was a fuzzy, furry monster!

It said, 'Oga poga, my name is Fuzz!'
'Hi, my name is Amy!' I said with a buzz.
I asked, 'Can I keep you a wee while?'
He replied, 'Yes,' with a cheerful smile.

So me and my monster started to play,
We went on our scooters and laughed all day.
But then at night, he had to go.
Out of my window and into the snow.

Amy Coats (9)
Milton Of Leys Primary School, Inverness

Monster Poem

I found a monster on a land.
Then he started to play with sand.
My monster was as fluffy as his mummy's tummy
It ate everything so I gave it some jelly.
And then he was seriously smelly.
I made him a bath and the bath was steaming.
He was in the bath, he ate the soap
And he couldn't cope.

When my monster was all dry
I started to ask him, 'Would you like a Scotch pie?'
He said, 'Yes.'
When he was done he started to roar
I said, 'Why are you roaring at me?'
But I realised he wanted to be my friend.
Then I said to him, 'You're so cute
I'm going to call you Dooby.'

Megan Baxter (9)
Milton Of Leys Primary School, Inverness

Candy Palava!

One evening I went to Paris
At the Eiffel Tower I saw
A pink perfect monster
I said, 'Hi' but it never replied.
Suddenly it started to cry.

I asked him what the matter was
He said, 'People are scared of me
As I look like a big, vicious giant
But really I'm fluffy and friendly and funny!'

The little monster said his name was Candy
But he was sneaky and cheeky,
He was as fluffy as a pillow pet,
I said, 'You are cute, cuddly and cool.'
I said, 'Let's be friends.'
Me and my monster
Play every day out in the sun
It's so much fun.

Leah Collingwood (9)
Milton Of Leys Primary School, Inverness

The Interactive Monster

There was once a mad, marvellous, magnificent monster
Who lived in Candyland.
He had some purple prickly prickles on his furry pink skin,
Glistening black eyes and his name is Doodle.
I met him in the wonderful weary woods
He asked me if I wanted to walk with him
I said, 'I would like that, thank you!'
So he trotted ahead of me
Then he asked me if I would like a smoothie
But it was no ordinary smoothie
It was the ultimate groovy geek smoothie
I said, 'The ultimate smoothie!
How cool is that?'
So we both had one
I thought he was melting
After he was actually floating up into the sky
He had gone so I walked home.

Then when I was asleep he was there
He accidentally knocked over my lighting lamp
Then I woke up and Doodle was not there.

Katie Grant (9)
Milton Of Leys Primary School, Inverness

Bobby's Adventure

I went to the spooky forest
It was dark and dangerous
I said, 'Hi' to the monster
And he was blue and two
He was as fluffy as a bunny.
He had sharp teeth like a nail
He had sparkly eyes like a diamond
I told him to come with me
He jumped into the car
Then Bobby jumped out of the car
I opened my door and ran after Bobby
Bobby saw the sun, he tried to grab the sun
But he was too small
Bobby wanted to go home
So I stopped at a hot drink shop
Me and Bobby had some hot chocolate
When he was finished I took Bobby home
He ran away, I went home.
I got ready for bed, I went to sleep
I said goodnight to Bobby
And Bobby said night too.

Brooke Fraser (8)
Milton Of Leys Primary School, Inverness

The Red Rampage

I found my monster on Mars
In a rocket to the stars,
I crash-landed on a town,
And my monster came out in a dressing gown,
He was big, he was tall,
He had just walked through the wall!

I took him down to Earth
And we started to play,
But he wanted to do everything
His very own way.
He eyes went red with rage
And then he started to rampage.

He ripped off his dressing gown
And destroyed the whole town,
Then he yelled something horrible up to the sky,
And I came up to him and shouted, 'Why?'
But the next thing he said made me cry!
'I will not rest until you are dead
Because I want to make you into a comfy bed!'

I ran away to call the fire brigade
It was as if the world was at war,
And it made me say, 'What on earth is this for?'
I dialled 999 so fast my fingers were a blur
'Get your biggest hose and cover my monster in fur!'
The plan worked like a charm
Because we managed to kill Onagatata and bury him in a farm!

Ewan Brown (9)
Milton Of Leys Primary School, Inverness

Bob Saves The Queen!

Once there was a monster who really loved to play,
'What's his name?' I hear you ask, why it's Bob Bay.
He lives near the hilltops, that's the same as me,
We try to meet every day but parents, what a pity!
Then one sunny evening we heard a high-pitched scream
We wondered who had screamed then we realised what it was
And it was the . . .*Queen!*
So . . . Bob raced down the hill and charged through the door
When he heard some villains shouting, 'More, more, more!'
He ran through the hall and crashed into a wall,
He got up off the floor and barged through another door
He turned left then right then he saw some fight, fight, fight
He didn't liked the sight of that,
So then *wham, wham, wham* with a baseball bat.

Owen MacDonald (8)
Milton Of Leys Primary School, Inverness

Mystery Monster

I had a monster, he was funny like a bunny.
He was great, he was my best mate.
He pings and flings stuff
He is lazy and crazy.
He can fly, he's my egg.
He runs round a tank
And it was blank
He is blue and his age is two.
He's in town with a clown
My monster is a ball
And he always goes to the mall.
He went to a hill
And saw his friend Phil.

Lennon Mackay (8)
Milton Of Leys Primary School, Inverness

Frizzle Fraz Poetry

I have just found a monster in a New York street
We found a bench and had a wee seat,
I took her to the shop, she took a sweet
We went on a plane, landed in the park
We started to play
She did everything her way.

She was as fluffy as a cloud
And she was very loud.
She jumped out and was very proud.
She asked me did I have a pound?
Yes, I have a pound it was very round.
We eventually got home
She turned over the table
Then started to nibble the table
It was fun.

Ellie Ross (9)
Milton Of Leys Primary School, Inverness

My Monster Poem

I have a friend called Jimmy.
He comes from the moon.
He looks quite evil and ugly too
I found him one sunny afternoon.

I took him to school.
The school was very cool.
All of a sudden he ate the chair.
Everyone started to stare.

Finally we said goodbye with a finger click
He disappeared in a nick.
It was very sad but I didn't cry
My little monster flew into the sky!

Ben Stainsby (9)
Milton Of Leys Primary School, Inverness

Saving The World

I was playing with my Play-Doh
Then a big red ball started to grow,
He was small and round,
He weighed about one pound,
He was kind and hyper
He had eyes as vicious as a viper,
He was creative as can be,
He danced around with me.

I asked him what's his name?
He never replied but I know he would some day,
He said he wanted to save the world
And find the precious pearl,
He said he's cool,
He made a pool so we could go,
And then we dived dangerously down.

We went to save the world,
We found the crystal pearl,
But then a giant robot came,
So we had a furious ferocious fight,
We took him down,
We won the crown,
But then he softly said he had to go,
With cheerful tears I said, 'Cheerio!'

Duncan (9)
Milton Of Leys Primary School, Inverness

My Monster Poem

When I woke up I saw a dark shadow.
It was big and scary
It came in my room
He told me his name, it was Dinimo
His teeth were sharp like a knife.
His eyes were like the ocean.
And his wings were like gold.

So then we were in the air
And soon landed in the funfair
We went on the Big Wheel
And it was made of steel.

So we were at my house
And Dinimo started turning wrinkly
He said, 'I need water!'
So I grabbed a bucket and poured it on him

A *bang* came from outside
We looked out the window
There was a fight I said
Dinimo flew down and took the swords out his side
And he was the winner of the fight
Then a spaceship came down and took Dinimo home
I hope I see him again.

Macy Mercer (9)
Milton Of Leys Primary School, Inverness

My New York Monster Adventure

One day in Central Park
I saw a movement in a bush
When I crept over I couldn't believe my eyes
It was a monster! His name was Jelly Bean
Fluffy like a cloud
Eyes like the sky above
And smelling like sweets!

We went to the shop
To buy Jelly Bean a top
But to my surprise
He turned everything into fluff!
It gave me a fright and a whirlwind of thoughts
We got in trouble from the shopkeeper
So we ran away into a field.

He started to dance wildly
It was hilarious
But then I realised there was
A UFO in the sky
We said goodbye
And that was the end
Of my monster adventure.

Katie Ward
Milton Of Leys Primary School, Inverness

My Monster

The monster appeared under my bed.
Happy and bright blue
'Hello there!' he said
With a body of slippery goo
I asked if he had friends
He replied, 'No not I.'
'Well we can be friends.'
'OK,' he sighed with a smile like my mum.

When I went to school
He jumped in my school bag without me knowing.
But little did I know he was looking cool!
When it was break
He jumped out and shouted, 'Surprise!'
As he got out of the crumpled bag
He started to eat everything
'No don't eat that,' then I started to nag.
'You are meant to eat food not anything.'
'But I'm hungry,' Squishy started to cry.

The bell rang to come in,
'Oh no you must hide.'
'But why?' Squishy said with a sigh.
'If the teacher catches you, who know what will happen?'
'Oh my!' Squishy yelled.
So Squishy hid away as the teacher came in.
'Hmm I thought I heard something.'
Then it was time to go
It was also time for Squishy to go,
'Goodbye,' he shouted.

Rhianna Parker (10)
Milton Of Leys Primary School, Inverness

My Ice Monster And Me

On Mount Everest, Mia and I
Saw a portal up in the sky!
We climbed up the stairs made of snow
And we went through the portal, off we go!

Through the portal was an icy world,
Filled with things to see,
A minute later, a monster jumped right behind me!

We got a fright, we ran away,
But the monster cried, 'Oh please stay!
I only want to play!'
We ran to her and asked, 'What's your name?'
'Ice Blast' she said and we started to play.

We went through the portal, through the dancing snow.
With Ice Blast yelling, 'Here we go!'
We went to town and had lots of fun
Now my poem is nearly done.

We ran to the portal, climbed up the stairs of snow.
My monster started to cry and said, 'Goodbye.'
My monster went through the portal as the wind blew
'Goodbye,' said Ice Blast, 'I will see you soon!'

Susan Gardocka (9)
Milton Of Leys Primary School, Inverness

112

The Friendly Monster

I'm a nice monster who's a whole lot of fun.
I mean a ton of fun.
And I'm going to meet with my very best friend.
Who I'm going to stay with for the weekend.
My friend is called Spiky,
My friend's cousin is called Mikey.
He's coming up as well
We are going to go to the wishing well.
I'm wishing for to go to my very own world
My friends can come too but who will get them to my world?
You know I'm going to lose the plot,
But if I lose the plot I will get shot.
So I may as well go to my friends.
We will party
But my friend changed his name to Marty.
I'll get there where they are
Let's go to the bar.
That was fun, oh no I'll have to go home
Now my friend said, 'OK.'
I think we will go to bed. Zzzzz.

Max Tasasiz (8)
Milton Of Leys Primary School, Inverness

I Found My Monster

I found him swimming with Jim.
We went home, I had to hide him.
We started to play with modelling clay.
He made a muppet monkey.

After, he got hungry.
I took him to the shop.
He bought apples, bananas, pizzas and oranges.
He forgot to pay, I ran after him, he was fast.
The police cornered him but the food was gone.

I got taken off to jail.
I knew I was in trouble
As my mum was as red as blood.

Charlie Lawson (9)
Milton Of Leys Primary School, Inverness

A Day With My Monster

I met my monster in my candyfloss
I nearly ate her up,
She was as pink as a pig
And as soft as a teddy
I had never seen anything like it
Nothing at all.

So I took her home,
Unfortunately she hates my brother
And my mum's furniture
'Boo hoo!' I said.

Then she started to roar.
We said, 'Be quiet our parents might hear!'
And downstairs she went
In big bags of tears.

So I gave her some food,
I took her back upstairs
I put her underneath my bed
'Goodnight,' I said.

Orla Buchanan (9)
Milton Of Leys Primary School, Inverness

Fuzzy Fin

I found my monster at the bottom of the sea
He was as fluffy as can be.
We played in the sea with a ball
Then me and my monster went to the mall.
Me and Monster bought jackets, jumpers and shoes you see
My monster absolutely adores me.
My monster has a fin and a tail,
My monster is a male.
Monster likes to spin round and round
But he doesn't like to be on the ground.
Then my monster said goodbye
I tried so hard not to cry
Then he said he had to swim
Going faster and faster with his great big fin.

Mia Cunningham (9)
Milton Of Leys Primary School, Inverness

Fuzzy

I was climbing the mountain
I heard little footsteps
I felt a spike and saw something red
I turned around to something small and very smelly
It was a red little monster
I took it home and my sister screamed!!
I said, 'Dinna wirry it's only a monster.'
'I ken, why is it in here though? Get it oot!' she said.
'Fine.' I said and tried to get it oot.
I said we were going to the haunted house,
But I took it to the mountain

Grace Wellwood Guy (8)
Monkton Primary School, Prestwick

Fuzzy Head's Day Out!

Lang lang ago I met a monster called Fuzzy Head
He had one ear which was green and he had a very hard head.
He also had big ugly lugs.
He loved cakes and bones from pirate bone soup.
He was a really naughty monster, we loved each other.
He was away to lunch with the Queen but he was really naughty
He threw cups of hot water at the Queen
He threw cakes and buckets at the Queen.
When she showed him around the palace
He threw down the cups and saucers
When he came back from the palace I heard a screaming noise
I smelt a minging smell it was Fuzzy Head
We went to a café, the monster had pirate bone soup
Fuzzy Head had cakes and I had soup.
'It was minging,' Fuzzy Head said,
After that we went to a cupcake competition
Fuzzy Head's favourite cupcake was the minging monster.

Emma Coulter (8)
Monkton Primary School, Prestwick

The Scary Squidge

Not that long ago I met a muckle monster
That came from space.
The monster had long lugs and muckle hands
And he is very nippet.
When I went into space I met a wee friend
That was horrible looking.
The monster let me touch the moon,
That was very nice of him.
We met another wee friend.
He was cute and cuddly.
We went for lunch on Planet Jupiter.
That was very nice,
But at the end of the day I had to say goodbye
I really enjoyed ma day.

Lauren Cooper (7)
Monkton Primary School, Prestwick

Mia And Zara

I found two wee monsters lying on the street
There were awfully kind so they turned
Into ma wee pet monsters.
Ma pink one was called Mia
And her friend that is purple was called Zara.
After a couple o' hours ma pink one and me went
to the cinema.
We went to see 'Frozen', it was good.
We went to have some jelly with the Queen after.
Ma monster got into trouble because she was being a loon.
We went back to Zara, the day was great!

Emily Wilson (8)
Monkton Primary School, Prestwick

The Red Monster

I was in the park
And I saw a red monster
He was so wee
His name was Fizz
He had long lugs,
Seven eyes
And he was smelly
Fizz has yellow eyes
He is cheeky to his mother
He eats jelly
He had orange horns
He went to the moon
He said he is fierce
So I've gotta hide Fizz
He lives in Zerg with his friends
He is also a haggis head
I waved bye-bye to him as he left.

Amy Holland (8)
Monkton Primary School, Prestwick

The Fizzy Monster

The Fizz monster lives in a cave
On top of a mountain.
He loves to eat rocks.
He's six feet tall
He loves to watch Horrid Henry on TV
People call him Stink Brain
But he's not even got a brain.

Reece Merry (8)
Monkton Primary School, Prestwick

Huggle Came To School

When I got up I was afraid because I saw a monster
With muckle horns, long ugly lugs and minging hair.
I went doon the stairs for breakfast
But there was nothing there
That was why he had a muckle belly.

I took him to school, all the wains were afraid
And he was afraid of the teacher
Because she was warty, muckle and minging.
Huggle was so afraid he ran out of the classroom
When it was lunch time Huggle took all the food
And the dinner lady was afraid.

When I got home from school I was glad Huggle went home
But I wanted him to come back.

Beth Kerr (8)
Monkton Primary School, Prestwick

Njl

One day I was at school
And I saw a great muckle giant!
It came into the school
He was a friendly giant
He said he lived in the ring of fire
He got called BFG (big friendly giant)
His real name was Nathan James Lydon
Sometimes he even got called NJL
He does not like water
He loved fire in the volcano
He could fly out to anywhere
When he comes out, the volcano erupts.

Nathan Lydon (8)
Monkton Primary School, Prestwick

Monster Poem

Long, long ago my family and I went to the aquarium
And we went to the sea monsters' park.
I thought it was just sharks and rays
But it was real monsters
Some sloopy and some slippery,
Some flat and only one dry.
I liked that one so I picked it up
And I saw it was the Loch Ness monster
I wanted to have it so I picked it up
But it dragged me under the sea
I saw mermaids and mermen and giant clams.

Laura Baker (7)
Monkton Primary School, Prestwick

Hairy Harry

On ma way to the cinema I spotted a muckle monster
His name was Hairy Harry and he hae a muckle doup.
His fangs were sharp, his lugs were muckle
His gut pouch hae a muckle bellybutton.
And he hae a muckle nik
And his hands were just flippers.
What good was he if he had no fingers?
I popped outside but the monster wasnae there
So I came back inside
And there were neep trails on the floor
And it seems like he's just gone for a beer.

Caitlin Taylor (9)
Monkton Primary School, Prestwick

The Red Monster

I was in the park and I saw a red monster
He was awfully wee
His name is Fizz.
He has long lugs, seven eyes, he's moody
Fizz has yellow eyes
He is cheeky to his mither.
He eats jelly
He has a giant gut pack
He goes to the moon
He said he is afraid
So I've gotta hide him
He lives in Zerg
With his friends.
He is also a haggis head
I waved bye-bye to him as he left.

Stephen McDonnell (7)
Monkton Primary School, Prestwick

The Jelly Bowl

I would like to tell you about my monster
I found him in a dark spooky place called a bowl of jelly
His name is Squidgy and I love him so much
I can't cuddle him because his jelly will go through my hands.
He has three friends called Blop, Blob and Bob.
Bob says, 'Dun, dun, booooop,'
When I feed him his jelly he gets bigger
His favourite is raspberry jelly.
He is scared of big rides and lions and elephants
Monkeys and dun, dun boooop hamsters.
I hope you like my monster, he is not scary at all
Just cute and cuddly. I hope you like my monster.

Lia Latimer (8)
Monkton Primary School, Prestwick

Squidgy

I was on my way to school
And on the way down I met a purple nice monster.
And he said ta me, 'I'm Squidgy and I'm harmless,
Can I come along and stay wi ye?'
'All right mate c'mon let's go.'

We started to introduce wee Squidgy
Ta my mither and father
They both liked him so we went tae the park.

Later that day his mither and father
Came ta pick him up from Earth
In a fancy gadget to go home.

Jacob Mullen (7)
Monkton Primary School, Prestwick

Hairy Harry The Muckle Monster

On ma way to the cinema I spotted a muckle monster
His name is Hairy Harry and he hae a muckle doup.
Hairy Harry is really nasty and he eats a lot of neeps
His lugs are awful long they nearly touch the ground.
Hairy Harry hae a twin sister, she hae red eyes
Even though she is his twin sister she hae seven heads.
There was this yucky drink that Hairy Harry gulped doon
Do you know what it did?
It made him good so he will always be nice
For the rest of his life.

Katie Baker (8)
Monkton Primary School, Prestwick

The Fuzzy Planet

One day I went to Planet Fuzzy Head
To go on an adventure.
I met a small fuzzy monster
Who had small lugs.
He had one leg,
He was very smiley and
I found him eating a burger.
We went exploring in the jungle
And we found his twin on a tree.

He was the same but smaller.
We found a burger tree in the distance
So we went to the tree,
But it was just a normal tree.

The monster likes putting on jackets
And has a small head.
When darkness fell,
we went back home.

Sandy Crann (8)
Monkton Primary School, Prestwick

The Rid Terror

Once I was on a zoo trip
I looked at the crocodiles
When a monster jumped out
From the water
And said, 'Can I come with you?'
At first I was scared
And then said, 'OK.'
We walked through the zoo
And all the wains were afraid
Because he's a bit of a loon
There he was ma wee rid terror!

Joseph Murray (7)
Monkton Primary School, Prestwick

Haggis Heed

There was a monster called Haggis Heed
He is fat and greedy
He likes jumping on me
He eats raw coos in ma hoose
He is my best friend.
He loves me and I love him.

One day Haggis Heed wanted to go swimming
I took him.
Then he wanted to go bowling
Then we went home.

Ben Thomson (8)
Monkton Primary School, Prestwick

![Young Writers]

Jelly Blob

I woke up on a rainy morning,
I stretched my long arms and saw
Ma monster Jelly Blob at the edge of ma bed!
He said to me,
'I've got an invitation from the Queen for lunch, can I go?'
He went and he saw the Queen.
The Queen glared at him, she ran away.
'I'd better just eat lunch here,' he said.
After lunch we went home.
I put Jelly in bed and he fell asleep, as snug as a bug.
I was tired tae. I got ready for bed.
I checked on Jelly Blob, I went to bed and fell asleep.

Grace Kerr (8)
Monkton Primary School, Prestwick

Messy Monster

Once there was a monster that lived in Cheesecake Land
And it was the monster that had the sharpest hand
Nobody would go near his dark, dark cave
Because he could never behave
Without dinner
He would get thinner
When he went out
A smell was going about
He smelt human
I thought *Oh no he's going to capture me.*
So he picked me up and took me to a place I never knew
Then I saw a pot of stew so I flung him in the boiling stew
I don't know how
But I've got that *boom, boom, pow!*

Hannah Robinson (9)
Onthank Primary School, Kilmarnock

124

Hairy Murray

I saw a shadow
It looked like a mallow
It was big
It looked like a pig
It's furry, it looks like Murray
We went to a show
We never wanted to go
We went to the park
And met my dog Spark
Spark started to bark
Because he was locked in the dark
Then we went on a trip
I hope my trousers don't rip
When we got some food
My dog said it wasn't good!

Amy MacDonald (10)
Onthank Primary School, Kilmarnock

Creeper The Friendly Monster

One day a monster as slimy as goo
Walked down the path
Which was as slidy as a slide,
Stinky as a toilet,
Spiky as a dinosaur
Wings like a fire-breathing dragon
So I said hello to him
Wanting to shake his hand
So both of us went for an ice cream
But his went in the goo.
We went to Legoland, Florida as well
My monster had to go home
It was still light, I said
'It's still day time!'
He went to the Lego shop
He bought me some Lego
And I never saw him again.

Charlie Muirhead (9)
Onthank Primary School, Kilmarnock

Something Mind Blowing

As fast as a cheetah,
As strong as a rhino,
As scary as a spider.
He could climb walls like a spider
But nothing could match him.
His body was round,
I heard him making a really scary voice.
He looked as cool as a cucumber.
He was so evil he could rip down a house like a tornado.
He was like a multicoloured rainbow.
This creative creature is really mind-blowing.
He could kill you in a flash.
He's like a sabre-toothed lion.
He's as round as a circle.
He's as bold as a frog.
He has fire on his feet like a volcano.

Kyle Stewart McCrone (9)
Onthank Primary School, Kilmarnock

Killson

My monster is from Gunland,
His friends are all from Funland
One day he went out to pay a man,
The man said, 'What are you doing here?'
'It's money from last year!
No! I know I should have taken it
But now for a little trip!
I hope my shoes don't rip'
Then we went and got some food
It was really good,
Now we are both full!
I think it's time to pull through!
Oh no! We've fallen in a hole!
Let's tell them to hold on to that pole!

Alicia Cree (9)
Onthank Primary School, Kilmarnock

Jump

One day I went to a monster shop
I looked around but one monster caught my eye.
She gave a hop and there was a horrible rot
So that was the monster I picked.
I called her Petal because she was a flower with legs.
'What?' I shrieked.
Then Petal said, 'What?'
'Ah,' I said.
She jumped out of her pot, 'Yippee!' she shouted.
I took her home in my car
But first we went to the Eiffel Tower.
We went to the top.
Suddenly Petal jumped up on a cloud.
'Stop, come back you will hurt yourself!' I said in horror.
There was a horrible sound . . . rain!
Then she started to fall out of the sky
But it got louder and heavier (hailstones)
Then I saw her at the bottom
She was a horrible scary monster.

Jenna Allan (9)
Onthank Primary School, Kilmarnock

Fluffy Woffy Monster

One morning I woke and I saw a monster
It disappeared and then he came back.
I met his pet.
I asked him his name
He was called Fluffy Woffy
I followed Fluffy Woffy around
Until he finally got there
And I asked Fluffy Woffy, 'Where are we?'
Fluffy said, 'We are in Australia'
We went home
It was disgusting and it was dirty
I didn't even want to be home
Then my mum cleaned it up.

Caitlyn Oueay (9)
Onthank Primary School, Kilmarnock

The Cupcake Land

It happened on a windy night
I heard a weird noise
It was loud as an elephant
But there was a cupcake portal
So I went in it.
Then there was a flash before my eyes
It was Cupcake Land
It was pretty like a princess
Then I saw a cupcake castle
There was a monster with a dragon head and feet
But a horse's body and tail
It was weird like a butterfly.
But the monster talked
It talked like a human
I didn't care
It was like talking to your pet but I whispered
It was cute like a hamster
So we went to save the Lollipops
They were sweet as a pumpkin
Their house was on fire
But when I put the fire out
They put a spell on me
I turned into a big scary, loud, red, giant that kills.

Emily Campbell (9)
Onthank Primary School, Kilmarnock

The Ugly Monster

Once there was a monster in Monster Land
And he looked scary with purple, yellow spots
He loved going to Pound Land
Lots of friends there and ugly too.
200 friends, one had red eyes
And it was a killer monster
When it eats it gets fatter and fatter
It eats human beings
We went on an adventure to Pant Land
He did not like Pant Land
He went to Dancing Land
The monster was a good dancer
He was a better dancer than me.
We went to lunch with the Queen and the prince
Then we went to Monster Land
We were playing tig and hide-and-seek
Then I went home
I heard the ugly monster yelling,
Screaming and screeching
He went to the land of human beings
The army and police came
It ate all the people
I went up to him, he picked me up
And he hugged me.

Tjay Hastings (9)
Onthank Primary School, Kilmarnock

It's Satan's Son!

I discovered Satan's son when walking down the road
As solid as steel in a crate, as white as a ghost
What a monster it was, so yellow and bright
With a staff and a submachine gun.
He looked bad but he was good.
We went on an adventure as mucky as a swamp
It was a forbidden temple up north
It was a bedrock
Satan was doing a ritual,
Very mysterious I thought
He summoned a demon
The demon saw me, he was easy to slay
With Hermous Morag anyway.
I heard a loud shout and a pooey smell
I felt my hands shaking, I tasted fear
There were more, as red as blood
Also as bloodthirsty as vampires.

Austin Reid (9)
Onthank Primary School, Kilmarnock

The Bad Monster

The monster is disgustingly green
And the monster ate the Queen
The monster's name is called Glorg
The monster's friends are called Clorg and Dorg
The monster is from Org
The monster dug in the sand and found a potato
And the monster also found a tomato
The monster went into his lair
And then scoffed down a pear
Then his friends ate some human hair
The monster made a big machine
Whilst his friends were at a dance routine
Then me, Roddy and Austin went into the lair
And killed the evil monster and his friends
Then me, Roddy and Austin went to the fair.

Alexander Leslie (9)
Onthank Primary School, Kilmarnock

The Feasty Beast

He was as cool as a cucumber
As hot as chilli and as smelly as a skunk
He had friends called Bob and Sam
He was an ugly scary monster
He has a hairy chest
Suddenly I heard *boom!*
So I went downstairs and the door was open
So I checked the living room and saw
A scary monster as scary as a crocodile
And as fast as a cheetah
He said, 'Do you want to help me save the Earth?'
I said, 'I'm not sure!'
Then I said, 'OK let's go!'
We went out the door and all I saw was lava.
So I said, 'We are going to die!'

Glenn McPheator (9)
Onthank Primary School, Kilmarnock

Wobbly Willy's Digger Day

There was once a monster who was a very big fan
Of a hot Australian/American band.
Wobbly Willy from Crazeville,
He went so crazy when he had to pay the bill.
He was so lazy he had to call his friend Phil
He said, 'Will you come and pay my bill?'
Phil said, 'No!' So he shouted through the phone,
'I'll get you some day one way or another!'
That day came.
Willy was walking towards Phil's house while he was talking.
Then Jenna, Devin, Caitlyn and I overheard him say,
'I'm going to kill Phil today!'
I said, 'He must be a killer!'
Jenna said, 'Isn't that the guy that stands at the pillar?'
Devin said, 'And his second name's Miller.'
He was digging a hole when he saw Phil with a bowl!
So he grabbed him and stabbed and threw him in the hole!

Eva McQuade (9)
Onthank Primary School, Kilmarnock

The Big Friendly Monster

He's a huge purple monster
His horns are red
In her dreams he haunts her
He's hiding under her bed
In the morning he is gone
She goes to bed
The next night
She tries to read a book
Will she get a fright
If she takes a look?
I wonder if he's there
She looks and sees huge kind eyes
That don't look scary in the end
And gets a big surprise
When he wants to be her friend
She'll never have a nasty dream again.

Liam Davies (10)
Onthank Primary School, Kilmarnock

Something Strange

I had a monster, his name was Jim
He never knew how to swim.
He thought he was cool
So he went in the pool
And that was the end of him
He tried again
But he failed again
So he took the train
And he shook in pain
Then it started to rain
He went to his cave
And he couldn't behave
And in that dark night
Something strange happened
He turned into an evil monster.

Louise Milligan (9)
Onthank Primary School, Kilmarnock

My Monster

I saw a big creature it was brown
With one eye and horns, plus a wing.
I had a piece of string
But that won't work
I thought he went to the kirk
We went to a café called McMuck
All the people ran out
So we went to Outlook
We got him an email
We got him a date on the dating website
When she met him she ran away
So me and my monster played Shaway
Then we put it away
But that was yesterday
Today his parents came and sadly took him away.

Meg Sinclair (9)
Onthank Primary School, Kilmarnock

The Horrifying Monster

The monster may look scary
But he is also very hairy
He may look long
But he smells like pong
And is very thin.
He may look like Gareth Bale
But he is very pale
And he whacks people
With his spiky tail
And he is a huge fail
His claws look like paws
And his teeth look like claws
His eye looks like a big red pie.

Kyle Bryden (10)
Onthank Primary School, Kilmarnock

Me And My Monster Meeting The Queen

My monster is called Little Lightning
He is faster than lightning
He's really scared in case he grows a beard
He doesn't want a beard.
He's really fuzzy, cute and always joyful.
We went to meet the lovely Queen.
But she was as skinny as a bean.
We went to sit at her table.
It smelled like a stinking stable.
We had her cupcakes and said 'Goodbye'
We went home to sing a song
But the house smelled like pong.
I know why my mum never cleaned it
It looked like a rugby pit
So then we all started to clean it up.

Tamzyn Thomson (9)
Onthank Primary School, Kilmarnock

Coconut

Coconut, Coconut, Coconut cracked!
Tiny and teeny with terrible temper
Furry and freaky, friendly and fuzzy
His roar so loud it scares the clouds
Beware not to hurt him, because he bites
Like William Wallace, he'll put up a fight
Brave Bunny, Boomba and Huggle Boom
Are his friends he likes,
We play at Wallace Monument
And swing from side to side
I wish I could take him back home to Bazzinga
Where I rule there as the king-a!

Brogan Henderson (9)
Riverside Primary School, Stirling

The Adventures Of Huggle Boom

'Defence mode activated,' said Huggle Boom
His bright lights glowed in the gloom
He quickly surveyed the room
We stayed bold
He began to loom
Then suddenly everything went cold

Huggle Boom don't hurt me with your spike
Can't you remember what it used to be like
When you were a small wee tyke?
So calm down, calm down
And to Italy we shall hike
To take away that frown.

Liam Fraser (9)
Riverside Primary School, Stirling

Puffy McDuffy

My monster is very puffy
He is small and very fluffy
Puffy McDuffy is very scruffy
But not as cute as a puppy
Sometime he can be very huffy
And also is very mucky.

When he goes to the park
And hears the dogs with a loud bark
He acts like a big fairy,
Because he thinks it's very scary
On the way home, he sees a shark
Then he's off as quick as a spark.

Erin Bechelli (9)
Riverside Primary School, Stirling

My Dream Monster

I met a monster fluffy and kind
He came from Mars and had a strange mind
We went to London to go to the fair
We went on a ride called the Magical Hare

We went on more rides and had hot dogs
And played games with sticks and frogs
After that we had some ice cream
Then I woke up and it was all a dream!

Callum Addison (9)
Riverside Primary School, Stirling

Monster McFuzz

Monster McFuzz is having a picnic.
Getting his food and going lick, lick, lick.
Eating with his friends McToot and McTick.
He's having so much fun.
Monster McFuzz only came for a lolly on a stick.
He's eaten all the buns!

They watched the parade,
And drank lemonade.
Who came to watch? The monster brigade!
Monster McFuzz waved and cheered.
Monsters danced as the monster band played.
McFuzz was thrilled when his friends appeared.

Georgina Robertson (9)
Riverside Primary School, Stirling

The Day I Met Fuzzy

Once when I was walking to school I met a monster.
She was cute but she was fluffy too.
She was blue and five feet two.
She was a nice friendly monster so I became her friend.
Fuzzy lived on Mars
She liked school so I took Fuzzy to school with me.
We did language and maths
Fuzzy said she loved it.
But she wasn't very good at maths.
When we were walking home from school
She met her friend.
They started talking about some party
I was worried in case she got lost on the way to the party.
The party was very soon and she didn't have any clothes to wear
She wanted to wear a dress so I let her borrow one of mine
And we went to the party together.

Kayleigh Trainer (8)
St Brendan's Primary RC School, Glasgow

Buddy

While outside playing a huge creepy monster appeared
With big ears and big eyes
I was surprised!
She said her name was Buddy Fuddy
And she wanted to be my friend.
She was pink, hairy and not a bit scary.
She is from Monster Land
I was looking for her and
She appeared and she was sad
She had no friends and no food
I found her food, I found her some friends
And she was happy again.

Sinead Monaghan (9)
St Brendan's Primary RC School, Glasgow

Fuzzy's Adventures On Earth

My monster is from Monster Land
And her name is Fuzzy Wuzzy.
I met her when I was walking to school
And she is about eight feet two.
She was cute, fuzzy, happy
And she wanted to be my friend.
Fuzzy likes to play hide-and-seek
So I played with her until I had to go home.
When I got home I looked out my room window
And saw Fuzzy, she looked up at me and waved.
She disappeared and I wanted to know where she was going
So I snuck out the house to see what she was doing
And I saw she had a new friend, her new friend was black as coal.
I hope Fuzzy will come back to me
Because I don't trust her new friend.
Her new friend was called Boo
And she came to my house to gobble me up
So I had no chance of being her friend again!

Leah McGill (8)
St Brendan's Primary RC School, Glasgow

Nine Eyed Monster

One night I was walking down the street
And saw a big huge monster.
His name is Gizzy Wizzy and he's about 6 feet 2.
He is from Neptune and has nine eyes
That are as white as snow.
He was very evil and scary
I ran like a van home.
I went to school and Gizzy Wizzy was at school too.
He ate all the food, teachers and tried to eat me.
I was a lot smarter than Gizzy Wizzy
So I went home and bent a stick
Then threw it at his spaceship then it vanished.

Kieran Hinton (8)
St Brendan's Primary RC School, Glasgow

The Devil

One day I was skydiving and my parachute burst.
I fell from the sky and I landed on a flying eye.
He was a monster called Devil
He was slimy, tiny and his wings were as black as coal.
We went to terrorise the city and blow up a skyscraper
But the skyscraper landed on me.
And someone shot him in the eye with a bow and arrow
And said, 'Bull's eye!'

Connor Hudson (8)
St Brendan's Primary RC School, Glasgow

The Adventures Of Doodle

One night there was a spooky spark
And my dad woke up the dog which made him bark.
I didn't wake up though, I did not know what was there.
The next day I looked around for the spooky spark.
My dog will bark if it finds it.
I felt something hit my head
I felt tired and went to bed.
I figured out what it was, it's a monster!
He is called Doodle.
I have known him for a day but now he is away.
I tried to find him but he is gone far away today.

Adam Gillon (8)
St Brendan's Primary RC School, Glasgow

Me And Doo Doo

His name is Doo Doo and he's friendly
I was on the bus and was scared it would gobble me up
But it was friendly
It was crying because it couldn't stop lying
It was eight feet nine, a slimy, ugly, hairy giant
It was from Monster Land
Then we went to Spain and people were screaming
But then I told them he's good
And then we went home and I kept it as a pet.

Jacob Seabright (8)
St Brendan's Primary RC School, Glasgow

My Fuzz Friend

One day I was at the park
When I saw a ball of fuzz!
It was as pink and fluffy as candyfloss
It said it was from Pom Pom Land
And her name was Fuzzle.
She was good and kind
I took her on an adventure to Poland.
I showed her to everyone I know.
We all agreed to take care of her.
We went to the beach,
The sand was a soft as a feather
There was also good weather.
We had some ice cream
We could smell the sea
But she said she had to leave me.
I was very sad
But she said she would come back.

Agata Knaak (8)
St Brendan's Primary RC School, Glasgow

The Boy Who Met A Monster

One day on my way home I met a monster.
His name was Oogy.
He was cute, fuzzy and liked to boogie.
He said he was from Jupiter.
He had light blue eyes
And he was the same size as me.
So I took him to the park
And I played with him every day.
Until one day he was gone!
I checked everywhere
Then I noticed he had gone away
And I was never friends with a monster again.

Connor Cassidy (7)
St Brendan's Primary RC School, Glasgow

Googley And Me

One day I was walking on a mountain and saw a cave.
We went in and saw a monster
My family ran but I stayed because I am brave.
He was hairy and scary, big and furry.
I took him to see my friends.
When we got there they all ran away.
They didn't know he wanted to have fun and play.
He asked if we could go to space and I said yes.
When we got there we were flying around
Then he said he was hungry
I took him to Harry's Hot Dogs.
He ordered a hot dog the size of a tree
And when he finished he gobbled up me!

John Smith (8)
St Brendan's Primary RC School, Glasgow

My Monster

My monster is called Gizzy Mizzy
I met him at a grave.
He was lonely and scared
So I took him to school
So he might be saved.
He was cute and fuzzy and friendly to me.
But he gobbled all the teachers up.
The next day we went to the park
We had fun until he gobbled me up.

Aidan Milne (8)
St Brendan's Primary RC School, Glasgow

Me And Blob

Last night I saw a blob
He looked like he didn't have a job.
He burst into tears and he had big ears
I was going to give him a hug
But I was too scared.
Then I heard a scratching noise
Coming from the monster's voice.
The very next day I saw it again
I was going to hug it but I was in a rush.
I was so sad he didn't even look bad.
Later I saw a blue slime trail
I followed it to a spaceship to another blob
Who didn't have a job.
Then they said, 'All aboard the spaceship to Zung!'
He flew off and I said,
'Oh but I hope it makes new friends on the planet Zung.'

Caleb Lyden (8)
St Brendan's Primary RC School, Glasgow

The Cute Little Girl And Cool Monster

One day while walking I found a cool cave.
I went in because I was brave.
I found Lightning.
She was ugly, fat and shone bright
Like a lightning bolt.
She was not friendly
She chased me to the park
And she licked my hand.
It poisoned me.
I saw Uncle Zurt and I went running to him
And I said, 'That dog poisoned me!'
Suddenly the monster came crying
I hurt its paw, it was bleeding.
I was helping. She said, 'Sorry.'
I said it was OK.

Ruby Gallagher (7)
St Brendan's Primary RC School, Glasgow

Gooy Looy

On the way to school I saw a monster
All slimy and gooey.
Its name was Gooy Looy.
He was about 8 feet 2.
He lived underground and was very mean.
His teeth were dark and very sharp.
We went to school and at playtime
He gobbled a tree the size of me.
But he was still hungry so he ate all of my friends.
I told him to stop but he kept going
Until he was so full he could have popped.
So I found a pin and *bang* he popped.

Kenzo Warren (7)
St Brendan's Primary RC School, Glasgow

Barry And Me

One afternoon a furry thing jumped out
He told me his name was Barry and he liked to shout
We went to the park to fly his kite
And I noticed his teeth were very white.
Everybody ran away but I stayed right there.
We went on the swings and he pushed me up
Then I found his favourite cup
I asked him how he found it?
He said he didn't know.
We went on his spaceship then we saw a farm.
He took me to the farm and said he would never do harm.

Kyle Irumwa (8)
St Brendan's Primary RC School, Glasgow

Mr Good

At the park
Playing football with a boy
Friendly, fast at kicking
Ugly and really hairy
After football
They have a tickle fight
Hee, hee, hee,
Ha, ha, ha,
Ho, ho, ho.
Back home very tired
Lying in bed watching TV
Monster is having a sleepover.

Callum Ross (5)
Shawhead Primary School, Dumfries

Scary Man

The monster was walking on his own
Smelly, angry, dangerous
He crashed down a house
Big *bang! Smash!*
Puppy phoned the police
They came and got the monster
Nee-naw, nee-naw
Locked up in prison
Just feeling sad
In for one night.

India Woods (5)
Shawhead Primary School, Dumfries

The Electronic Alien

One day I saw a monster
His name was TX
He is covered in diamonds
He is naughty
Angry and electric
He whacked someone with a stick
Everyone ran away
'Roar, I am going to eat that tree!'
Someone was hiding behind
Tiny ate the tree *crunch!*
The person ran
Tiny flies off in a spaceship
Off to play with his friends
Everyone was happy now.

Samuel Johnstone-Wilcox (7)
Shawhead Primary School, Dumfries

The Monster At The Park

One day I saw a monster at the park
He was really fluffy
And had lovely fur
He had a pointy tooth
But I didn't mind
I knew he was a nice monster
So we went swimming
The monster's fluff went all straight
We played with a beach ball
Throwing to each other
We had to get out
The monster dried his fur
And I brushed my hair
We decided that he was my friend
We slept in the same bedroom.
We went to sleep
The owl yawned
We were very tired
After the day at the swimming pool.

Emily Jahn (7)
Shawhead Primary School, Dumfries

The Lost Monster

One day a monster went for a picnic
He was cute and fuzzy
He munched on his food
When he went home he got lost
He was sad
'Where's my cave?'
He walked and walked and walked
He turned out at Dumfries
He got angry, 'Roar!'
Smashing the ground
Then I went past
I stopped
I walked over very scared
He calmed down
'Where do you live?' I said,
'Africa.'
'Come to the beach.'
A hundred miles over the sea
We collected wood for a raft
We sailed away home
A happy monster again.

Harry Greenwood (7)
Shawhead Primary School, Dumfries

The Football Bear

In a town far away,
Lived a bear that liked to play,
Everywhere and every day.

He went to a football stadium
And met a man who was Canadian,
The man put him in a team,
Which was actually kind of mean.

The bear left the team and joined another,
This team was very nice,
But all they did was give him head lice!

He joined another and wished for luck
But all he saw was . . . a bunch of ducks.

He joined one more and hoped for luck
It worked! The team he was in was very good,
Very good indeed,
This was the thing he needed!

So the bear was very happy,
And hoped that he would win the trophy!

Noah Henry (11)
Strathpeffer Primary School, Strathpeffer

A Strange Friend

He's good, not bad,
He likes to play,
But sometimes he runs away,
I try to find him; he's just not there,
He sneaks behind me and gives me a scare.

He likes to fetch, he likes to run,
Who knows, maybe he likes chewing gum?
He has a chew
He blows a bubble,
I guess I'm right, he does like chewing gum!

I went off on an adventure,
To find his home,
Nobody is there,
Oh no!

He lifts me up,
And gives me a cuddle,
Puts me to bed,
And says, 'Goodnight.'

Emily Forrest (10)
Strathpeffer Primary School, Strathpeffer

The Monster Who Wanted To Sing

My monster he is blue,
He lives at the bottom of the loo,
Its tummy is pink,
He loves ice rinks,
But he wants to learn something;
It is to sing!
So he climbed to the top of the loo,
Wondering what to do,
'Help me to sing.'
'OK,' I said,
'Go, laaah.'
He went, 'Aahhh.'
But he soon learned.
'It's time to go,' I said.
He screamed, 'Nooo!'
'But you have got to go.'
'I don't want to.'
'But it's your home!
Goodbye Huggles.'
'Bye,' he said, 'see you soon.'
So off he went,
But he came back after a while,
He moved in as happy as could be,
Now he lives in my room, in his very own cage.

Jody MacLean (10)
Strathpeffer Primary School, Strathpeffer

Meeting The Pom-Pom

His name is Sherbet and he is pink and round,
And he likes to bounce up and down on the ground.
He has nothing to do and nothing to play,
But one day in the heat of the sun,
He bounced away to find something fun.

On the way he met a little girl,
The little girl's name was Sandy Pearl,
Sherbet stayed until the end of the day,
But . . . Sherbet missed his home!
So he bounced back home again.

Elsa Fearn (10)
Strathpeffer Primary School, Strathpeffer

Fuzzball Land

Snuggles is small and green and blue,
With green eyes,
If you are playing a game with him he will always offer a clue
When we play hide-and-seek he said, 'Don't peek!'

One sunny day,
We went on an adventure to find his home.
We went up and down,
Following the trail.

It got dark after a while,
We walked for nearly a mile,
Until at last, we found it!

We went inside and shouted,
'Is anyone in?' No one was in.
Snuggles brought me a drink,
And gave me a wink,
And before I knew it, I was back home.

Nicole Nicol (10)
Strathpeffer Primary School, Strathpeffer

A Monster Called Bob

Once there was a pink monster called Bob,
Who was fluffy and fuzzy and fun,
With a black, curly 'tache as dark as night.

One day he bounced along the street,
Saying hello to the people he would meet
Then he bounced onto the beach and met me.

He fell into the hole I made; I pulled him out of the hole
We played on the beach for hours and hours,
Then we went home and to bed.

Me and my monster are very good friends.

Lara Lamont (10)
Strathpeffer Primary School, Strathpeffer

Meeting Shelby

Shelby the alien was born one day,
On space she lay,
He mum led her astray
She stayed there lying for days.

Shelby has glowing green eyes,
She eats lots of space pies,
She never tells any lies
She has swingin' green thighs!

Fire she breathed
People always scream,
She always dreamed,
That she would be queen.

Her lashes were long
She lived above Hong Kong,
Her fire is strong,
She likes to play ping-pong!

She has nobody to play with,
People think that she is a myth,
But she loves Joey Essex's quiff!

Tigerlily Potter (10)
Strathpeffer Primary School, Strathpeffer

The Monster That Likes Green

She loves green
And she is quite mean
She hates being unseen
She thinks she's so fine
And she hates the number nine.

Charlie Carlin (9)
Strone Primary School, Dunoon

The Day I Met A Monster

I was walking home when something caught my eye
It was a little monster eating a blackberry pie.
He had an axe with a blade made of steel,
And I was afraid because it looked quite real
He had sharp teeth and could breathe fire
I'm not sure I could trust him he looked like a liar
But looks can deceive so I gave him a chance,
I walked right up to him as if in a trance
He stared right at me his eyes glued to my face
I couldn't run he would beat me in a race
I went up towards him but he ran away
And that's the last that I saw him till this very day.

Owen Danks (10)
Strone Primary School, Dunoon

Furball

Down the hill and round the corner,
There lived a lawyer
His fur was orange
His shape was ghost-like
His name was Furball
Oh and his tongue was furry
He had some fashion
And a little passion.

Kimberley Frederick (10)
Strone Primary School, Dunoon

Soul Ripped From Me

Up high in the sky, above the sea
Plummeting down to Italy.
A big purple head, body so red
Humongous and ugly, so it was said.
Knocked out cold, put on a boat
Set to sail and hopefully float
Docked at Wales he ripped down the sails
And threw the crew overboard
And as he roared
I jumped in the sea
Shouting, 'Help me!'
I swam for my life
As his scorpion tail sliced the knife
I felt a pain
As I shouted again
When it was too late
My soul was ripped from me.

Duncan Morgan (11)
Strone Primary School, Dunoon

Fluffpuff Meets Robbybobby

Fluffpuff was walking home one day
When she bumped into Robbybobby
She told Robbybobby that he had to go
Or she would call Mo,
The town's policeman.
She said that Mo would kick a can
If Robbybobby didn't go.
Then Robbybobby went boldly
And popping down the street
Just as he walks up the plank to ship
Fluffpuff calls him back
Robbybobby asked her to marry him
She said yes and now they live together.

Abigail Stone (11)
Strone Primary School, Dunoon

George The Monster From Mars

George is a monster from Mars
His kind is up in the stars.
Sometimes he wants to go home,
To his planet that looks like a stone.
He is stuck on Earth,
In a place called Perth.
Because his parents left him alone
And let him rot to the bone.
In a spaceship that landed on my house
And almost killed a mouse
Maybe you've seen him before.

Ciaran Danks (11)
Strone Primary School, Dunoon

Ninji Ninga

Once there was a monster
Who was walking down the street
He grabbed his nunchucks
And hit people in the feet
He went to the ninja shop
And bought himself a knife
The customers who were in there
Begged for their life
Ninji Ninga really wasn't kind
Everyone was scared of him
But he didn't mind.

Campbell Morgan (9)
Strone Primary School, Dunoon

Chuff

Mr Chuff lives in the sand
He's a lovely monster
And gives people a hand.
Building sandcastles are his favourite thing
He helps his friends and he likes to sing
Pang the crocodile swims in the lake
He shouts to Chuff, 'For goodness sake!
You need to come in and enjoy the fun
It's great in the water in the sun.'

Cameron Harding (9)
Strone Primary School, Dunoon

Fuggle McPuffle

Fuggle McPuffle was as small as can be
He was born in the year 1993
He was sad, grumpy and alone,
There wasn't a need to use his mobile phone.
He was different, chaotic, sulky and sad,
He thought to himself, *why don't people like me even a tad?*
He had no friends, not at all,
Until one day he received a phone call
It was a yeti called Spaghetti
Wondering if he was OK
'No' he said, 'I don't have any friends not since May.'
'I could come over, what do you say?'
'I'd like that, see you later today.'
Fuggle McPuffle finally found a friend,
And this time he wasn't pretend.

Cerys Hayes (11)
Stuartfield School, Peterhead

Sneaky Slithe

Sneaky Slithe lives in a dark and scary cave
With mice, rats and bats which make him rave
One day after he woke up
He made his dark and scary cave erupt
Except not with lava but with happiness and laughter
And instead of scales he wore some fur
He put the word out that there was a party at his place
Lots of people came which put jubilation on his face
After it he had millions of friends
And this is how this sensational story ends.

Isaac McLean (11)
Stuartfield School, Peterhead

Rube-Axele The Monster

His eyes shine bright late in the night.
Whilst his ears are as big as the moon
They even say he was born with the silver spoon.
He washes in water, he dries in sand
But nothing could beat the skills with his hand.
He sings a song like ding, dong and thinks it's awful merry.
He bought a toy and thought *oh joy this could be fun*
But when he picked it up it weighed a ton
So he put it back to the store
And, 'No more toys for a while,' he said,
'I think I'll stop or I'll bump my head.'

Brooke Erridge (11)
Stuartfield School, Peterhead

Untitled

The devilish PM makes bad decisions
Like no monster poetry competitions
His teeth like sharp spikes
And writes with pencils like pikes
His graphs frighten even the canniest o' politicians
And he also turns the tax to the max
People say he punches politicians purple.

Scott Robertson (11)
Stuartfield School, Peterhead

Purple Puncher

Purple Puncher punches for lunch
Purple Puncher loves to munch
Purple Puncher with giant feet
Purple Puncher loves to eat
Purple Puncher tried to fly
Purple Puncher sadly died.

Jamie Kindness (11)
Stuartfield School, Peterhead

Spikey's Day

Spiky woke up, said 'What's up?'
Then someone replied, 'Where's my cup?'
Next came lunch and some brunch
Spiky did not have it because he would just crunch.
Last but not least came supper
Spiky is starving but at least he's not harming.

Nicholas Elrick (10)
Stuartfield School, Peterhead

Under My Bed

One quiet night
I spotted the thing
That gave me such a fright.

It was under the bed
The monster with purple and green spots
Mum said it was in my head
Though I knew on her glasses were dots

He only growled
With his one eye
And as the wolf howled
I said my final goodbye
And crawled under the bed.

Georgia Hay (11)
Stuartfield School, Peterhead

The Ruthless Gladiator

The Gladiator took a riot at anything in sight
Maybe anything as high as a kite
He jumped down to the watery stream
And blew out a fiery beam
Then he jumped down to a drainage pipe
It was all dirty and looked like it needed a wipe
He ran through the gruesome, smelly pipe
The police ran through the cold night
He ran through a wall and appeared at a beach
Where the police were out of his reach
He looked at his face in the water
As the police began to wonder
They could hear a roar from the ocean
Then they could tell his emotion
The creature confused and angry.

Caillen McLean (12)
Stuartfield School, Peterhead

Scary Sid

Scary Sid has no friend
He finds it hard to make friends
He tries and tries but no luck
Then one day Scary Sid made a friend
And they have been friends forever.

Kelly Rebecca (10)
Stuartfield School, Peterhead

Shibeadador

I was walking along the beach
When I saw a creature as blue as the sky
It flew past me and dropped a message for me to see
I read *Shibeadador Fluffolab*
He came down in a mini lab
Then he landed on a slab.

The creature came towards me
While his eye floating on top of his head sparkled in the sun
His fluff made a cute complexion
He spoke his name and flew up into the sky's selection
The creature landed on a cloud.
Suddenly shouted, 'See you another day, maybe in May
For your birthday!'

Sophie McCallum (12)
Stuartfield School, Peterhead

The Frost Skull

Once upon a time there was a monster called Jeff.
He lived in a place called Frosty Woods.
He had a cape as cold as death
An arm covered with ice crystals
His bones were blue as frost,
His face was a skull
It was like you are staring at the face of death.
He has a magic staff with a dying star,
Shiny and bright as the sun
He wore an old battle helmet
In the end he was the guard of the woods
Protecting it for thousands of years
He was the last of the Frost Skull.

Jack Bain (12)
Stuartfield School, Peterhead

Monster

The other day
I met a monster
Her name was Tamera
She was half human
Half monster,
My ma was producing
Her new album
I got her autograph
And a photo with her,
Now we go tae all her concerts,
And get VIP passes,
And front row seats,
Ya belter!

Aasiyah Rehman (11)
Tollbrae Primary School, Airdrie

Monster

One day
I met a monster,
A tottie monster,
A no fair monster,
That monster,
Is a mental monster,
That monster,
Is a feart monster,
Why are you scared?
No other monster is scared!
That monster.

Anthony Fitzgerald (12)
Tollbrae Primary School, Airdrie

Tae A Moanster

Most of ye are mental,
Most are wee and tottie,
Then there are the nutters,
The nutters are dafties,
Almost all of ye are crabbit,
Some of ye are braw an' bonnie,
Some of ye are nasty an'
Wave yer bahookie at us!
Yer aw thick heided,
But even if
Yer aw mental, tottie and wee,
Nutters an' dafties
Crabbit an' bonnie,
Nasty an' eejits
We're all feart of ye all.

Cameron MacPherson (11)
Tollbrae Primary School, Airdrie

Four Eyes

He's ugly,
He's not scared,
He's called . . . Four Eyes
He's looking for his true love,
He goes through the houses,
Up the mountains,
And through the woods,
Anything gets in the way . . .
It's war!

Daniel Stanners (11)
Tollbrae Primary School, Airdrie

Tae A Monster

Look at the wee, tottie thing,
Sitting,
Sitting on the bus,
Looking fir a nice place tae live,
Moving around,
When he finds a place,
The villagers chase him out of it,
He's always on the bus,
But he is so wee,
I dinnae know how they see him,
He's a wee bonnie guy,
Way a big gub,
A wee, daft, crabbit monster,
Just sitting,
Sitting on the bus.

Donald Obre (11)
Tollbrae Primary School, Airdrie

Wan Day

A met a monster,
A tottie, feart, mental monster,
A monster wae three big, beady eyes,
Wan blue, wan green and the ither broon,
A dinnae recommend making him angry,
If you dae, he'll gobble ye up,
And there will be nothing left
So,
Be careful,
In case ye meet,
The monster a met.

Erin O'Neill (11)
Tollbrae Primary School, Airdrie

Monster

I meet a monster,
A scary lookin', sleekit monster,
A look it him,
He looks it me,
His wan eye burns into me,
I draw ma mace,
He bares his fangs,
Then I notice
Behind him hangs
Some dead dwarfs
Just like me,
But I'm a dwarf, I dinnae flee,
After that
It wis money I gained,
Because the monster wisnae seen again.

Jamie Ford (11)
Tollbrae Primary School, Airdrie

Pookie

What can I say
About my wee Pookie?
Everyone thinks he's rather spooky,
But Pookie is nice and Pookie is sweet,
He's rather shy until you meet,
Go up to the Highlands in your car,
You can see him from afar,
If you see him you are lucky,
As he's always fighting with Mr Pucky,
Mr Pucky is bad, My Pucky is mean,
He's very rarely ever seen,
Just remember,
Do not run,
Because he doesn't
Think it's fun.

Rebecca Milton (12)
Tollbrae Primary School, Airdrie

Young Writers Information

We hope you have enjoyed reading this book – and that you will continue to in the coming years.

If you're a young writer who enjoys reading and creative writing, or the parent of an enthusiastic poet or story writer, do visit our website www.youngwriters.co.uk. Here you will find free competitions, workshops and games, as well as recommended reads, a poetry glossary and our blog.

If you would like to order further copies of this book, or any of our other titles, then please give us a call or visit **www.youngwriters.co.uk.**

Young Writers
Remus House
Coltsfoot Drive
Peterborough
PE2 9BF
(01733) 890066 / 898110
info@youngwriters.co.uk